Pavlov and Freud: II

SIGMUND FREUD

BY THE SAME AUTHOR

Process and Unreality
Pragmatism

PAVLOV AND FREUD
Vol. I. *Ivan P. Pavlov: Toward a
Scientific Psychology and Psychiatry*

PAVLOV AND FREUD: II

SIGMUND FREUD

A Pavlovian Critique

By HARRY K. WELLS

INTERNATIONAL PUBLISHERS
New York

*In Memory of My Mother
Who Loved Science*

LIBRARY OF CONGRESS CATALOG CARD NUMBER: 60-9949

© *by* INTERNATIONAL PUBLISHERS CO., INC., 1960
PRINTED IN THE UNITED STATES OF AMERICA

CONTENTS

PREFACE   7

I. SIGMUND FREUD   10
Freud as Physiologist and Neurologist, 12; In Search of the Dynamic Trauma, 16; The Discovery of Psychoanalysis, 22; The Elaboration of Psychoanalysis, 25; Later Years, 29

II. THE INTERPRETATION OF DREAMS AND THE SALIVARY REFLEX   39
The Salivary Fistula and the Dream Fistula, 41; Pavlov's Salivary Fistula in Operation, 43; Freud's Dream Fistula in Operation, 45

III. THE THEORY OF REPRESSION, PSYCHIC ENERGY AND THE CONDITIONED REFLEX   53
Freud's Theory of Repression, 53; Pavlov's Theory of the Conditioned Reflex, 61; Confrontation of the Two Theories, 66

IV. INSTINCTS AND UNCONDITIONED REFLEXES   69
Freud's Theory of Instincts, 70; Pavlov's Theory of the Unconditioned Reflex, 74

V. THE UNCONSCIOUS AND THE SCIENCE OF HIGHER NERVOUS ACTIVITY   79
Freud's Three Systems of Mental Activity, 79; Pavlov's Three Systems of Higher Nervous Activity, 87; Confrontation of the Two Systems, 94

VI. SLEEP, DREAMS AND HYPNOSIS   100
Freud's Theory of Hypnosis, Hypnotic Suggestion, Sleep and Dreams, 100; Pavlov's Theory of Sleep, Dreams, Hypnosis and Hypnotic Suggestion, 106; Confrontation, 110

VII. THE PSYCHOLOGICAL LINEAGE OF FREUD AND PAVLOV   113
Freud's Approach to Psychology, 113; Pavlov's Approach to Psychology, 122

VIII. FREUD'S APPROACH TO THE
TWO MAIN PROBLEMS OF PSYCHOLOGY   132
From Primitive Mind to Civilized Mind, 134; From Infant Mind to Adult Mind, 145; The Oedipus Complex, 149

IX. PAVLOV'S APPROACH TO THE
TWO MAIN PROBLEMS OF PSYCHOLOGY   159
Do Animals Think? 160; Infant Mind to Adult Mind, 168; Confrontation, 176

X. FREUD'S APPROACH TO MENTAL ILLNESS   179
Freud's Childhood Seduction Theory of Neurosis and its Collapse, 185

XI. PAVLOV'S APPROACH TO MENTAL ILLNESS   208
Pavlov's Pathophysiological Investigation of Some Neurotic Symptoms, 209; Confrontation, 215

XII. PAVLOV AND FREUD   221
An Evaluation of Freud in Terms of His Own Work, 221; An Evaluation of Freud by Comparison with any Objective Approach to Psychology and Psychotherapy, 227; An Evaluation of Freud Confronted by Pavlov, 230; A Comparison of the Lives of Pavlov and Freud, 232; Philosophical, Scientific and Historical Significance, 235; Toward a Scientific Psychology and Psychiatry, 237

REFERENCE NOTES   243

INDEX   249

PREFACE

PAVLOV AND FREUD, each in his own way, were striving to fill one of the last great gaps in human knowledge. The story of these two efforts on a grand scale, told in juxtaposition, is one of the most illuminating and at the same time fascinating tales in the annals of science.

The gap in question is the one which most immediately concerns each and every one of us as human beings, for it is the lacuna in our knowledge of ourselves: The nature of mind and its relation to the body, in health and in illness. Pavlov and Freud were pioneers in the attempt to put psychology and functional psychiatry on a firm scientific basis.

The manner in which each approached the problem, however, was so divergent as to form a direct opposition. While Pavlov sought the solution to the enigma of mental processes and their disturbed states in the functioning of the upper regions of the nervous system, Freud on the contrary pursued the same objectives within the limits of the mind itself, without regard to knowledge of the brain as the organ of mental life. Pavlov employed the experimental method of natural science to discover the facts and laws of the reflex activity of the brain, while Freud sought to discover the dynamics of mental processes by probing minds, his own and his patients'. The result in each case was termed by its author "a new science." Pavlov called his "the science of higher nervous activity;" Freud called his "the science of unconscious mental activity." Each claimed to have established the basis on which psychology and functional psychiatry could be transformed from primarily descriptive disciplines into mature sciences.

Around these two giant figures, with their sharply opposed approaches and theories, there has been developing over the past decades a general polarization of psychological and psychiatric thought. Pavlov serves as the pole attracting the various objective, experimental "schools," and Freud as the pole attracting the various subjective, introspective "schools." Each has wide influence throughout the world, including academic and medical circles, and each exerts profound influence on a number of related fields such as child development, education, anthropology, sociology, philosophy, literature and the arts.

It is of no small importance, therefore, that the claims of the two protagonists be examined with a view to determining the validity of each. Does the Pavlovian science of higher nervous activity hold the hope of mankind for an understanding of mental life and mental illness, or should this hope be entrusted to Freudian psychoanalysis? Or is there some middle ground uniting the best elements of both?

To answer these questions requires a careful examination and comparison of the life and work of Pavlov and of Freud. The two men lived and worked in the same historical period. In fact, their long and productive lives began and ended in approximately the same decades: Pavlov, 1848-1936; and Freud, 1856-1939. Both lives span the divorce, near the close of the last century, of psychology from the mother field of philosophy, and its birth as an independent discipline. Almost the entire history of modern psychology is closely interwoven, directly and indirectly, with the influence of these two men.

An examination of the life and work of Pavlov was completed in the first volume of *Pavlov and Freud,* published in 1956: *Ivan P. Pavlov: Toward a Scientific Psychology and Psychiatry.* An examination of the life and work of Sigmund Freud, together with a confrontation of the two bodies of thought, is the subject-matter of the present volume.

It is important to note an intentional limitation in the subject-matter of the present volume. Here the exclusive concern is to present a confrontation of the work of Sigmund Freud by that of Ivan P. Pavlov. There is therefore no attempt to examine the more recent developments in psychoanalysis. Nor is there any treatment of the rise and development of psychoanalysis in the United States or of its application in the various sciences and arts. These questions require separate attention and together constitute the subject-matter of a forthcoming book.

There is a further limitation in the present volume in the presentation of the Pavlovian science of higher nervous activity as it confronts the Freudian system. For a more detailed treatment of Pavlov's work the reader is referred to Volume I of *Pavlov and Freud*.

An objection to the main theme of the book may be raised, namely, that the respective approaches of Freud and Pavlov are so disparate as to be totally incomparable. Contrary to such an opinion the author seeks to demonstrate that the two meet and clash squarely in at least six major areas: instincts, sleep and dreams, hypnosis and hypnotic suggestion and neurosis. The confrontation of Freud's theories by those of Pavlov take place primarily in these areas.

Perhaps the major limitation in the book is the fact that the author is neither a psychiatrist, psychologist nor a physiologist, but a philosopher. This means that the arguments and conclusions remain at a general rather than the specific and detailed level, which may have its advantages as well as disadvantages. The volume is in fact a defense of scientific methods and concepts in man's attempt to understand himself in mental health and mental illness.

Chapter I
SIGMUND FREUD

SIGMUND FREUD WAS born, seven years after Pavlov, on the sixth of May, 1856, in the little town of Freiberg, Moravia, then a province of Austria, now a part of Czechoslovakia. He was the first child of Jacob and Amalia Freud. Jacob was a wool merchant and Amalia was his second wife, less than half his age. The Freud family, including grandparents, aunts and uncles, and half-brothers and sisters made up a significant segment of the two per cent Jewish population of Freiberg.

By the time Sigmund was born, his father had become a "free thinker," no longer attending the synagogue. He believed firmly that all wonders could be explained by science and that human reason would some day make a world free of prejudice in which all men would be equal. Jacob's forebears had been forced to migrate back and forth across the map of Europe in the face of persecutions and pogroms, but Jacob was convinced that the ideas of the French Revolution, "Liberty, Equality, Brotherhood," would finally be realized. For three years following the revolution of 1848 there had seemed to be progress in this direction, but then came the Restoration and Austria entered an extended period of extreme reaction, including violent forms of anti-Semitism. Under this pressure, Jacob moved his family, first to Leipzig for a year and then to Leopoldstadt, the Vienna Ghetto, for life. Sigmund at the time was four years old.

Reading, writing and arithmetic were learned at home, and young Sigmund did not go to school until he was ten years old, when he went directly into what would correspond to junior high school. Throughout his school years he brought home all the first prizes and was graduated from high school with highest honors at the age of seventeen. At this early age he was faced with the serious problem of choosing a career.

The youthful Freud was a hard-working student and voracious reader. He had already mastered several languages including Latin, Greek, English and Hebrew. Under the current fermentation around Darwin's theory of evolution and specifically inflenced by Goethe's poem on *Nature*—"Nature, nature, nature gives the answer to all secrets"—his first choice was science. For a Viennese Jew, however, the pursuit of "pure" science was out of the question. The only careers open to Jews at the time were business, law and medicine. He chose medicine and entered the University of Vienna in the Fall of 1873.

He was not particularly drawn to medicine and indeed appears to have had a rather strong aversion to it. He pursued his medical studies in such a half-hearted fashion that it took him eight years to qualify for his medical degree. Much of that time was spent in the physiology laboratory. Thus unofficially at least he was making a career of science. This was due not only to his own predilection, but also to the influence of a great scientist and teacher, Ernst Brücke.

Professor Brücke was director of the Institute of Physiology at the University and an exponent of the militant scientific movement known as the Helmholtz school of medicine. This movement was founded by four world-renowned physiologists: Emil Du Bois-Reymond, Herman Helmholtz, Carl Ludwig and Ernst Brücke. These men were dedicated to an uncompromising struggle against vitalism with its mystical concepts of "life-forces," "spirits," "essences," "psychic forces" and "entelechies," and its teleological interpretation of biological evolution and growth. The movement represented by the four scientists was atheist and materialist in orientation. The young Freud became an ardent and confirmed follower of Brücke and the Helmholtz school. He was thus at this time an atheist, a materialist and a scientific physiologist. He adhered to the pledge made earlier by the founders of the movement and which became the cornerstone of contemporary physiological materialism: "No other forces than the common physical-chemical ones are active within the organism. In those cases which cannot at the time be explained by these forces one has either to find the specific way or form of their action by means of the physical-mathematical method or to assume new forces equal in dignity to the chemical-physical forces inherent in matter, reducible to the force of attraction and repulsion."[1]

Closely connected with this dynamic movement in physiology was a thoroughly evolutionary orientation. Hundreds of researchers were busy filling the gaps in knowledge of the phylogenetic development from unicellular organisms to the higher animals including man. Here too the emphasis was on physical energies, causes and effects to the complete exclusion of nonmaterial forces, anthropomorphic plans and divine purposes. Darwin was the guiding light. It was an exciting, challenging movement and the student Freud was part of it. As Ernest Jones, his biographer, put it "Freud became for a while a radical materialist."[2] The first half of his life was devoted to physiology and neurology, with no little success in both fields.

FREUD AS PHYSIOLOGIST AND NEUROLOGIST

After some two years as a university student, Freud in 1876 began the first of a series of original research projects extending over a period of nearly twenty years. Carl Claus, director of the Institute of Comparative Anatomy, suggested that he make a study of the gonadic structure of eels. No mature male eel had as yet been found and thus no one had ever seen the testes of an eel. Freud spent a year in the laboratory of the Institute and at the Marine Station in Trieste dissecting some four hundred specimens. His findings were inconclusive and yet sufficiently significant to be reported by Professor Claus to the Vienna Academy of Science and to be published in its *Bulletin*. This was the first of many scientific contributions to appear in print under Freud's name.

In 1876, at the age of twenty, Freud was admitted to Brücke's Institute of Physiology as a research scholar. Brücke set Freud the task of investigating microscopically the histology of nerve cells. Over a period of five years he made important observations, summarized in a number of papers, which came close to formulating the neurone theory. Brücke read the papers at sessions of the Vienna Academy and they were published in the *Bulletin*. Thus Freud was one of the unsung pioneers of the neurone theory, the cornerstone of modern neurology.

In the course of these researches Freud made two improvements in investigative technique, the first a modification of the Reichert formula for preparing nervous tissue for microscopic examination and the second, the gold chloride method of staining tissue.

Through all this work Freud relied solely on the microscope and not at all on experimentation. Careful observation seemed to be his preference and forte. Throughout the twenty years of his *scientific* career, he shunned experimental tasks with few exceptions. One of the latter was in 1878 in Solomon Stricker's laboratory. Stricker was generally credited in large part with transforming pathology from a descriptive discipline into an experimental science. In Stricker's Pathological Institute, Freud was assigned to carry out experiments on acinous glands. In 1879 Stricker reported to the Academy that Freud had conducted experiments on these glands for six months but had accomplished nothing. Freud returned to his microscope more convinced than ever that he should confine himself to observation.

Finally in 1881 he received his medical degree, but it brought no immediate change in his life, since he was in no hurry to become a practitioner. For a year and a half longer he continued to work in the Physiological Institute and was promoted to the position of demonstrator involving some teaching responsibilities. In the normal course of events he could have expected further promotions — Assistant, then Assistant Professor and finally Professor of physiology in his beloved Institute. There were however a number of obstacles. First and foremost was the insuperable one of anti-Semitism. A career in physiology was out of the question for a Jew. Second, Brücke had two young assistants who would have to resign or die before Freud could be further promoted. Third, Freud had no financial resources to tide him over the lean years of waiting. His father had lost his small capital in the crash of 1873, and the young student had had to borrow heavily to finance his education. Finally, he had met Martha Bernays and they were engaged to be married.

He had now to think seriously of making a living. The only answer seemed to be to establish himself in private medical practice as soon as possible. For this he needed hospital internship and residency. Thus in July, 1882, Freud resigned from Brücke's Institute and began a three-year tour of duty in the General

Hospital of Vienna. It was a difficult decision for the young doctor-scientist since it meant substituting "applied" for "pure" science. In point of fact, he had, of course, little choice.

At the hospital he served for six months in Nothnagel's Division of Internal Medicine and then was transferred to Theodore Meynert's Psychiatric Clinic. The latter was the only strictly psychiatric experience he had in his entire life. He detested both the hospital routine and the treatment of patients, whether internal or psychiatric. He concluded that he was "just not made to be a doctor." With this in mind he had soon convinced Meynert to admit him to his laboratory where he could return at least in part to scientific work.

In Brücke's Institute Freud had investigated the phylogenetic development of the spinal cord. Now he concentrated for two years on the ontological development of the brain, particularly of the *medulla oblongata,* from infancy to maturity. The result of this work was three papers published in neurological journals which began to establish his reputation as an outstanding neurologist.

In 1885 Freud completed the requirements for the coveted appointment of *Privatdocent* in neurology at the University of Vienna by passing all the written and oral examinations and delivering a public lecture on "The Medullary Tracts of the Brain." The great Brücke had not only sponsored his candidacy but had made a special and impassioned intercession before the faculty committee on his behalf which carried Freud to victory over the other candidates. He was now twenty-nine years old.

On the basis of his research work and his appointment as Docent, Freud won a travelling grant and spent four and one-half months in Charcot's laboratory at the Sâlpetriére in Paris.

Jean Martin Charcot was one of the most noted neurologists of the nineteenth century. He was Professor of pathological anatomy in the Medical Faculty of the University of Paris and Director of the famous Sâlpetriére Neurological Clinic. Students came from all parts of the world to study under him. In his later years he had turned his attention to the functional forms of mental illness, those involving no organic lesions due to injury or disease.

At the Sâlpetriére Freud made a study of hysteria, particularly of the paralysis that in certain cases accompanies the illness. He learned to distinguish between organic paralysis and the functional form, and soon could recognize an organic or an hysterical patient almost at a glance. He knew the cause of the former, a physical trauma or injury, but what caused hysterical paralysis? He asked this question of Dr. Charcot and received the answer that it was a *dynamic trauma*. The only meaning that he could elicit from his teacher was that it was a trauma that *could not be seen*.

From this point on for almost a decade Freud's life was divided between a continuation of his neurological work and a quest for the meaning of the "unseen," "dynamic trauma" as the cause of functional mental illness. The latter was of course to become the passion of his life and the subject-matter to which he devoted his last forty years.

Before leaving the Sâlpetriére Freud made arrangements to translate Charcot's latest book, *New Lectures on the Diseases of the Nervous System*. He was a rapid translator and finished the task in July, 1886.

About this time he wrote the first part of a projected but never completed book on neuropathology, and a little later began work on a volume devoted to the anatomy of the brain, also abandoned.

Prior to going to Paris Freud had been offered the post of Director of a neurological clinic in the new Institute for Children's Diseases in Vienna. He had accepted and now upon returning home he took up his duties which continued for many years. For the next five years he was busy with family interests and professional work. In this period he published only one paper, a report on two rare cases of hemianopsia in children (1888).

For some time Freud had been interested in the problem of asphasia or paralysis of speech. In 1891 he published a book on the subject, entitled simply *Asphasia*, which was a highly valuable neurological contribution. His reputation as an outstanding neurologist was growing. In the next four years he published eight papers and monographs on cerebral paralysis in children which established him as the leading world authority on the subject. Recognition of this status came through a commission from the famous Dr. Nothnagel to write the section on "Infantile Cerebral Paralysis" for the latter's great *Encyclopedia of Medicine*. Freud did not finish this assignment until 1897. It was his last contribution to neurology and to materialist science in the tradition of his teacher, Brücke, and the Helmholtz school of medicine. Already he was deeply involved in the quest for the unseen, immaterial dynamic trauma said by Charcot to be the cause of neurosis. Thus ended at the age of forty-one a most promising career in the science of nervous diseases. Freud's name, however, will long be recorded in the annals of neurology.

In Search of the Dynamic Trauma

After studying with Charcot in Paris, Freud had stopped over in Hamburg where in the spring of 1886 he and Martha Bernays were married. The two then went on to Vienna to set up housekeeping and open an office where Freud could treat those suffering from nervous diseases. His office was actually one room of their small furnished apartment, for the young couple had little money with which to start either a home or a medical practice. He hung out his shingle as a specialist in nervous disorders, and settled back to wait for patients.

Freud, however, had worries other than financial ones. He knew that very few of the patients coming to a nerve specialist's office would be suffering from organic lesions. Most would be ambulatory cases of neurosis of one kind or another. How was he to treat them when the nature, not to mention the cure, of this non-organic, functional illness was unknown to him or to anyone else? Behind this practical worry about treatment lay the theoretical question: Why do people without actual injury or disease fall ill? To solve the practical problem of treatment of neurotics, the theoretical question had, of course, first to be solved. But Freud was faced with the necessity for immediate prescriptions and so he had to try this and that without theoretical guidance, to see if he could find something which would somehow work to alleviate suffering: sulphate of quinine, oil of turpentine, rest, exercise, hot baths, cold baths, massage, colored glasses, electric sparks. None produced the slightest result. The patients paid their fees and went on suffering.

For two years Freud floundered from one failure to another, and then in 1888 he read a book which turned him once and for all away from physical and medicinal forms of therapy. It was a volume on hypnosis entitled *Suggestion and Its Application as a Therapy* by Dr. Hippolyte Bernheim. Dr. Bernheim was one of Charcot's former students now practicing in the General Hospital in Nancy, France. He had discovered a country physician, Dr. A. A. Liébault, who was treating neurotics by means of hypnotic suggestion. In his book Dr. Bernheim described in detail how Dr. Liébault used hypnotic suggestion as a form of therapy and reported that he, himself, was convinced of its efficacy. Here for the first time since the days of the famous Mesmer, hypnotic suggestion was being taken seriously by a respectable member of the medical profession. Freud, with his uninterrupted record of failures using other methods, was greatly impressed by Dr. Bernheim's book, and at once decided to try the method on his own patients. The results were startling. In the first few weeks he achieved some overnight *cures* bordering on the miraculous and word quickly spread around the city of Vienna that Dr. Freud was a miracle-worker.

After the first flush of success, however, the old pattern of failure began anew. It appeared that some patients simply could not be hypnotized at all, while others could be put into only a very superficial hypnotic state. Freud concluded that his technique was at fault and that he needed experienced help. He decided to pay a visit to Bernheim and Liébault in Nancy. He spent several weeks in the summer of 1889 at Nancy watching Dr. Liébault at work among the rural poor and Dr. Bernheim in the hospital. He was greatly impressed by what he saw. Patients were put under hypnosis reaching the stage of somnambulism with amensia and then it was suggested, or sometimes commanded, that they would no longer feel their symptoms. Upon awaking, the symptoms for the time being at least were gone. Freud returned to Vienna with greater enthusiasm than ever for the method of hynotic suggestion. But more important for his future, he had, in his own words, "received the profoundest impression of the possibility that there could be powerful mental processes which nevertheless remained hidden from the consciousness of men."[3]

Back home and at work with his patients, Freud's enthusiasm once more gave way gradually to scepticism. Although he had occasional brilliant successes, he found that even in these cases the cure tended to be short-lived. The conviction grew that hypnotic suggestion was in fact a fraud practiced upon the patient. Still more serious was the realization that the method was a groping in the dark with success or failure as the only criterion, and that it tended to prevent any real scientific study of neuroses and their causes. It was not helping him in the slightest to discover that *dynamic trauma* of which Charcot had spoken, and which was the real passion of his life.

Just when the impasse in the search seemed completely impenetrable, Freud recalled a conversation he had years before with an old friend, Dr. Joseph Breuer. Dr. Breuer had told him about a case of hysteria which he had treated in an unusual manner and with startling results. Freud at the time had been deeply impressed and when he was in Paris had spoken to Charcot about it. But the old master had not shown the slightest interest and Freud had dropped the matter there. Now, in 1891, however, he turned once more to Dr. Breuer and made him recount the entire case history. The patient had been a young woman who had fallen ill while nursing her dying father, and when Breuer had taken over the case she was suffering from paralysis, inhibitions and states of mental confusion. Quite by accident Breuer discovered that the states of confused thinking disappeared whenever she was able to express in words the particular fantasy that had hold of her at the moment. He put her into a deep hypnotic state and made her tell him each time what it was that was oppressing her mind.

Breuer told Freud that the patient was completely incapable in the waking state of making any connection between her symptoms and the various experiences of her life. But under hypnosis she was able to supply the missing links. According to Breuer, all her symptoms went back to events connected with her father's illness and were in fact reminiscences of those emotional situations. Most of the memories, he said, centered around some thought or action which under the circumstances had had to be suppressed, and Breuer viewed the symptoms as substitutes for the suppressed impulses the patient had experienced. The theory was that a symptom took the place of an impulse which could not be carried into action under the circumstances of nursing her father. For example, when she had an impulse to dance, localized paralysis took the place of actual dancing. This was the famous case of Anna O.

Here, at last, Freud felt, was the dynamic trauma for which he had been searching. A psychic injury was caused by the necessity to repress a strong impulse, while the physical symptoms were substitutes for the action that would have been appropriate to the impulse. Freud's excitement and enthusiasm were boundless. Breuer's discovery, he maintained, was the solution to the problem of the "uncaused disease" known as neurosis. But that was not all, for Breuer claimed also to have discovered a method of treating the illness. He reported that when under hypnosis the patient recalled the situation, and when she went through all the emotions appropriate to the suppressed impulse, the associated symptom was abolished and did not return. Breuer called this form of therapy "catharsis."

From the moment he grasped the significance of Breuer's method, Freud used it to treat his own patients. In a period of two years he added four histories to Breuer's, and the two doctors collaborated on a book entitled *Studies in Hysteria,* published in 1895. In a joint introduction the authors outlined their theory, not yet psychoanalysis, but a long step in that direction. It stressed the significance of the emotions and the importance of distinguishing between conscious and unconscious mental acts, and introduced a dynamic factor by assuming that there is a constant amount of what they called "psychic energy" which must find an outlet. If it does not find an outlet, if it is dammed up, as it were, the equivalent energy emerges as a pathological symptom. The therapeutic aim of the cathartic method was to provide that the "psychic energy," which had been diverted to originating and maintaining the symptom, should be directed back on the normal path along which it could be discharged. When this was accomplished, the symptom, according to the authors, disappeared. Here was the seed that was to germinate in the mind of Sigmund Freud and emerge eventually as the full-fledged theory of psychoanalysis.

Freud, however, was not yet prepared to abandon his scientific training in physiology and neurology and to ascend into the sphere of *pure* psychology. One month after the publication of *Studies in Hysteria* he set to work feverishly on what is now known simply as *The Project*. There was a temporary lack of patients in the summer of 1895 and he wrote day and night for a period of several weeks. The manuscript was sent to his friend, Wilhelm Fliess, and lay buried for years. The English translation was not published until 1954. *The Project* was Freud's final and desperate attempt to keep his feet firmly planted on the ground of natural science.

In his introduction to *The Project,* Freud wrote, "The intention of this project is to furnish us with a psychology which shall be a natural science: its aim, that is, is to represent psychical processes as quantitatively determined states of specifiable material particles and so to make them plain and void of contradictions." And he added "the material particles in question are the neurones."[4]

His manuscript, some ninety pages, is an attempt to construct speculatively a physiology of the brain in terms of neuroses and their functioning. For our purposes it is not necessary to follow the details of his reasoning, but it is interesting to note that he allocated central roles to the processes of excitation and inhibition. The latter he called "the principle of neuronic inertia," and the only evidence he cites for it is that some such process is required if there is to be a science of the brain. The entire work is an attempt to *deduce* a theory of cerebral functioning, completely without the aid of experimental facts. On the basis of what little was known of the structure and function of the higher parts of the brain, Freud constructed an entire theoretical edifice in an attempt to account materialistically for all the major aspects of the psyche, from sensation and perception to thought and the emotions. But as the manuscript clearly shows, Freud was painfully aware of the arbitrary nature of his attempt and soon gave up the task, never to return to it.

The *Project* is somewhat similar, on a modest scale, to the work of James Rush. When Rush wrote his treatise on the *Human Intellect* in 1863, however, speculation about the physiological processes underlying mental activity was a necessary and helpful stage in the development of the science of the brain.

Anatomy, neurology and physiology had not progressed sufficiently to make possible a fully experimental approach to cerebral functioning. But in 1895 the situation was quite different. All the scientific requisites were present which made feasible an experimental approach to cerebral physiology. As a matter of fact, at the very time Freud was writing his speculative physiology, Ivan Pavlov was beginning those experiments which were to lead to the discovery of the physiological basis of man's mental life. To rely on speculation when a science is not yet possible is one thing; to make speculative constructions when the conditions exist for the birth of that science, is quite another. Thus the theoretical speculations of a James Rush or an I. M. Sechenov[5] in the 1860's were mileposts on the road to science, while Freud's 1895 *Project* was in effect a substitute for the experimental work that at the time needed to be done.

This is not to say that Freud should have, or could have, carried out the experimental tasks requisite for the establishment of a physiology of the higher parts of the brain. Indeed, he could not in any event have accomplished the feat, for he was in no sense a trained experimental physiologist. His scientific work had been in neurological anatomy where observation through the microscope, not experimentation, had been the main reliance. *The Project* bears witness that Freud was enough of a scientist to know where the real answers could be found to his questions about the "uncaused disease" of neurosis. His tragedy was that he was not able to do the necessary work. He could only speculate, which he did in *The Project*.

All Pavlov's training, on the other hand, had prepared him to undertake the monumental task of establishing the science of higher nervous activity. By 1895 he had already worked more than twenty years as an experimental physiologist. The logic of his life and work led him toward the discovery of the laws of motion of cerebral functioning.

Freud's abandonment of his *Project* bore witness to two stubborn facts: That in 1895 there was as yet no established physiology of the higher parts of the brain; and that Freud himself was not equipped to embark on its discovery. But at the same time he was consumed with a passion to discover the cause of neuroses. The logic of his life and work, in the years immediately preceding the abortive *Project*, led him to seek answers beyond the borderline of experimental science.

The Discovery of Psychoanalysis

From 1895 on, Freud was of necessity a dualist with regard to body and mind. On the one hand, he consistently maintained that the brain is the organ of man's psychic life, that without it there could be no thoughts or feelings. But on the other hand he held with equal consistency that, since little was known about the functioning of the brain, psychology had to be pursued as though it were a study entirely independent of cerebral physiology. Thus in 1898 he wrote: "I have no inclination at all to keep the domain of the psychological floating, as it were, in the air, without any organic foundation. But I have no knowledge, neither theoretically nor therapeutically, beyond that conviction, so I have to conduct myself as if I had only the psychological before me."[6]

Throughout his life Freud made many similar statements all contending that psychology had the right to pursue the study of the human mind independent of brain physiology so long as the latter was inadequately developed. The clearest of these statements is to be found in a paper he wrote in 1915 on *The Unconscious*. Speaking of the dependence of mental activity on the brain, he says: "Research has afforded irrefutable proof that mental activity is bound up with the function of the brain as with that of no other organ. . . . But every attempt to deduce from these facts a localization of mental processes, every endeavor to think of ideas as stored up in nerve-cells and of excitations as passing along nerve-fibers, has completely miscarried. . . . Here there is an hiatus which at present cannot be filled, nor is it one of the tasks of psychology to fill it. Our mental topography has for the present nothing to do with anatomy; it is concerned not with anatomical locations, but with regions in the mental apparatus, irrespective of their possible position in the body. In this respect then our work is untrammeled and may proceed according to its own requirements."[7]

Freud was convinced that science would one day discover the nature of the cerebral functioning underlying mental activity, and never tired of cautioning psychologists that they "must keep free of any alien preconceptions of an anatomical, chemical or physiological nature, and work throughout with purely psychological auxiliary hypotheses."[8] Freud was not a *philosophical* dualist, for he affirmed that mental activity was dependent on physiological motion in the brain. But he was an *operational* dualist since he proceeded on the assumption that in spite of the lack of a science of the brain the laws of mental life could be discovered by resorting to "purely psychological auxiliary hypotheses." He *operated* on the theory that mental activity was not dependent on brain activity, while at the same time he *philosophized* that the former was dependent on the latter. The problems of his practice and his grand passion to discover the dynamic trauma drove him to disregard the philosophy and enter the realm of pure psychology.

With *The Project* out of the way, Freud once more turned his full attention to his neurotic patients. He was now treating them exclusively by Breuer's cathartic method, urging them, under hypnosis, to relive the emotions which supposedly had led to the illness and thereby drain away the "psychic energy" supporting the neurotic symptoms. But as time went on grave doubts grew in his mind with regard to hypnosis as a means to catharsis. He found that apparent cures could be completely wiped out if his personal relation with the patient became disturbed. As a result, he decided to give up the hypnotic method entirely. But where was he to find a substitute?

In searching for an answer he recalled an experiment he had seen Dr. Bernheim perform. Bernheim had insisted that memories lay hidden in the human mind and that if sufficient patience and insistence were employed they could be brought to consciousness. To prove his point, he had made one of his patients recall at first hesitantly and then in a flood of words some traumatic experience which had until then been forgotten, and he had done it without the use of hypnosis, simply by insisting and by gently laying his hand on the patient's forehead. Freud decided to try this "urging" method on his patients.

The question before Freud was: "How had it come about that the patients had forgotten so many of the facts of their internal and external lives but could nevertheless recollect them if a particular technique [the urging method] was applied?"[9] He turned to his practice for an answer, and found, to his satisfaction, that in every case what had been forgotten was in some way or other painful to the person under treatment. The thought or the impulse had been either alarming, shameful or disagreeable to the subject, and therefore had not been allowed to remain in his consciousness. On the basis of this observation he proceeded to construct his theory of repression.

The first step was to account for the normal or healthy mental process, and from that to reconstruct the development of a pathological condition.

Freud represented the normal mental process as following a prescribed course: When an alarming or shameful impulse arises in a person's mind, it is at once opposed by other powerful tendencies. The two forces, the impulse and the tendencies resisting the impulse, would, he conjectured, struggle with one another in the full light of consciousness until such time as the impulse was repudiated and the "charge of psychic energy" was thereby withdrawn from it. In the normally functioning mind, this would be the end of the matter. No ill effects would ensue because the charge of psychic energy was fully withdrawn from the unacceptable impulse.

In a neurosis, on the other hand, the outcome of the struggle between the shameful impulse and the resisting tendencies, as depicted by Freud, was quite different. Instead of a more or less protracted conscious struggle between the two forces, the impulse would be debarred from access to consciousness almost as soon as it arose. But the "charge of psychic energy" would not be withdrawn from it and therefore the now unconscious impulse would retain its full force. The psychically charged unconscious impulse would remain to haunt consciousness, and would sooner or later find circuitous ways to discharge bits of its energy. These circuitous ways of discharge would, according to Freud, constitute the symptoms of the neurosis. He called this process *repression*.

Here at long last, Freud felt, was in truth the dynamic trauma of which Charcot had spoken. At the base of neurosis was no physiological state, but a purely mental one. Repression was the causal mechanism of the so-called "uncaused disease." Freud was jubilant. His great search had, he was convinced, ended in complete success. It remained only to fill in the details of the theory.

The *shameful impulses* of this early stage of Freud's thoughts were soon to become "the instincts" in his matured theory, particularly the sexual instinct and the death instinct; and the *other powerful tendencies* were later viewed as inherent in the so-called "super-ego" or conscience. Unconscious as an adjective was replaced by "The Unconscious" located spatially somewhere in the mind. Thus the theory of repression was elaborated in the years following 1896.

Freud's most immediate concern at the time was to develop a new form of therapy for his neurotic patients, and the theory of repression held some obvious implications. If a person was suffering from neurosis, it meant, according to this theory, that repressed unconscious impulses and thoughts retained their original charge of "psychic energy." The task of therapy was clearly indicated: the "psychic charge" must be withdrawn, or at least provided with an acceptable manner of release. To accomplish the neutralization of the "charge of psychic energy," the repressed impulse had first to be uncovered. This latter process involved considerable analysis of the psyche. Such probing introspection Freud called *psycho-analysis*.

In this way psychoanalysis was "discovered." Its immediate forebears were *hypnotic suggestion* and the cathartic method employed by Breuer in the case of Anna O. But in 1896 only the bare skeletal frame was born. Some forty years were required to round out the body of the system.

The Elaboration of Psychoanalysis

From the discovery of psychoanalysis in 1896 until 1902 Freud worked alone. His isolation was almost complete. On the one hand, he was cut off from the medical profession by his nonmedical approach to functional mental illness, and on the other, he had not as yet found the disciples that were later to gather around him in such ample numbers. It was a solitary six-year period devoted to the first elaboration of the theory and method of analysis.

He had constructed his theory of repression in the course of employing the urging method of probing his patients' minds. He soon found, however, that this method was inadequate to cope with the resistances to the recall of repressed material. Impulses that had been expelled from consciousness but had retained their so-called "charges of psychic energy" were found to be exceedingly difficult to bring back into consciousness. The method of hypnotic suggestion had concealed the resistances, while the urging method had proved powerless before them. Some method had to be found which could break down, or at least circumvent, the resistance of the patient to recall what he had previously forced out of his consciousness.

In rapid succession Freud found three such methods: Free association, interpretation of dreams, and transference. All three were held to be ways in which repressed material in disguised forms can enter consciousness through circumventing the resistance. Together, they constitute the essential psychoanalytical technique employed down to the present time.

Free association is an attempt to catch the censor, the conscience or the super-ego, off-guard by spontaneous, unthinking, unstructured associations. The patient is instructed to say whatever comes into his mind without eliminating any thought or image as irrelevant or embarrassing. In short he must talk without premeditation or judgment. In this manner, words, phrases and images may sneak past the mental censor and thus furnish the analyst with symbols which can then be interpreted in such a way as to reveal their unconscious meanings. The technique of interpretation centers around the translation of stereotyped symbols, the so-called primordial language of the unconscious. The art of analysis is twofold: First material from the unconscious must be collected, and second this material must be interpreted by means of symbol translation. Free association is one of the methods for collecting material from the unconscious, which can then be interpreted.

Dreams, for Freud, performed a similar function. Like associations involving unintentional thoughts, the imagery of dreams furnished symbolic allusions which formed the subject-matter of both free association and interpretation. Freud called the dream imagery "the manifest dream" and that which was symbolized by the imagery, "the dream thought." The symbolic images of the manifest dream required interpretation to arrive at the dream thought. The latter was supposed to reveal repressed and unconscious wishes. Just as free association was designed to allow the involuntary thought to enter consciousness in an unguarded moment, so dreams were supposed by Freud to catch consciousness in the relatively unguarded time of sleep, and thus allow passage of symbolic clues to unconscious repressed material. Thus he employed the imagery of dreams to obtain symbolic material which he could then submit to the art of interpretation.

The third method of psychoanalysis developed by Freud was what he called "transference." The intimate relationship between the analyst and the patient, the result of complete self-revelation on the part of the latter, leads to an intense emotional relationship between the patient and the analyst ranging from sensual love to embittered defiance and hatred. Freud's interpretation of this phenomenon is that the patient is reenacting the emotions of a former situation the memory of which is now repressed. The transferred emotions are supposed to furnish clues to the unconscious repressed material. Here again the clues require the art of interpretation.

All three methods of psychoanalysis are, according to Freud, primarily means to obtaining materials for interpretation. He interpreted them as hieroglyphic messages from otherwise inaccessible unconscious repressions.

Underlying the methods of psychoanalysis and the art of interpretation was Freud's theory of neurosis. Neurotic symptoms, the chronic phobias, obsessions, paralyses and others, were held by Freud to be among the devious ways in which repressed thoughts, impulses or wishes, retaining their irrepressible "charges of psychic energy," forced their way to discharge, either psychically or somatically or both at once. With regard to therapy, Freud held that the problem was to make the unconscious accessible to consciousness. When this is done, by means of the three methods and the interpretation of their materials, the symptoms are supposed to disappear because when repressions are finally made conscious, the theory is that the "charges of psychic energy" are thereby detached.

The culmination of his work during this lonely period was the writing of his major book, *The Interpretation of Dreams,* published in 1900. Freud maintained that dreams constituted the best evidence for his theory that repression is the key to both normal and neurotic mental phenomena. Since dreams are common to all people whether in illness or in health they became the focal point of his system. For psychoanalysis was never meant by its founder to be limited to psychopathology, but was intended as an all-embracing psychological philosophy which would account for the normal as well as the neurotic, for social as well as individual behavior, for civilization, science and art. Through the interpretation of dreams (see Chapter II) he wanted to demonstrate that repression was the key to the understanding of mental life in general.

In 1904 there appeared what is generally considered to be Freud's most popular work, *Psychopathology of Everyday Life*.[10] In it he applied his theory of repression to such things as forgetting of proper names, slips of tongue and of pen, and erroneous and faulty acts. All the above are treated by Freud as among the devious ways, along with dreams and neuroses, in which repressed impulses, thoughts and wishes force entrance into consciousness. For example, if a name slips your mind it may mean that you do not *really* like the person involved, or that you wish him out of the way. The emotion or the wish, having been previously banished from consciousness as objectionable, forces its way back in the disguise of forgetting. (See Chapter III.)

Freud had by now represented five phenomena which he held to be ways in which repressed material seeks disguised entry into consciousness: Through free associations; through transferrences; through dreams; through neurotic symptoms; and through forgetting or slips of the tongue, pen and their like. In 1905 he added still another. This time it was jokes, and the title of the book was *Wit and Its Relation to the Unconscious*.[11] Jokes, puns and witticisms of all kinds were treated, like the other five phenomena, as furtive ways of repressed material to gain admittance to consciousness. The subject-matter of wit, Freud maintained, is primarily seduction and aggression, and repressed impulses and wishes to attack and to seduce are often enabled to break into consciousness under the guise of jokes.

The six phenomena — involuntary associations, transferred

emotions, dreams, neurotic symptoms, forgetting, and jokes — are, in Freud's view, primarily methods of circumventing the censorial conscience guarding the approaches to consciousness.

LATER YEARS

The last twenty years of Freud's life were in large part devoted to supplying the philosophical framework underlying his theory of repression and the six ways in which it is circumvented. He called this philosophy "metapsychology." He developed his metapsychology in innumerable short papers and in the following books: *Beyond the Pleasure Principle* (1920); *Group Psychology and the Analysis of the Ego* (1921); *The Ego and the Id* (1923); and *Civilization and Its Discontents* (1929).

In the construction of his metapsychology Freud was more than ever acutely aware of the non-scientific character of his thinking. Thus in the middle of one of his theoretical constructs he pauses to say: "The indefiniteness of all our discussions on what we describe as metapsychology is of course due to the fact that we know nothing of the excitatory process that takes place in the elements of the psychical systems, and that we do not feel justified in framing any hypothesis on the subject. We are consequently operating all the time with a large unknown quantity, which we are obliged to carry over into every new formula."[12] This did not, however, deter him in his attempt to build an all-inclusive psychological system.

The theory of repression requires that there be a censorial guardian standing between The Unconscious and consciousness. In his later works he calls the censorial guardian the "super-ego," and he renames The Unconscious the "id." The super-ego is the ideal built up by the conscious ego out of legal, ethical, moral and religious prohibitions and imperatives. It is the conscience of the earlier works. In the light of the demands of the super-ego, the ego represses instinctual impulses which might threaten or conflict with the ideal.

The ego or consciousness represents reason and light while the id or The Unconscious represents irrationality and darkness, unknown and essentially unknowable. Ego-consciousness is under the impression that it reacts to the external world according to true knowledge or what Freud calls "the reality principle," but according to him this is largely self-delusion. The conscious-ego, with all its reason and science, is really for the most part doing the disguised bidding of the unconscious id with its instincts of sex and aggression or death. "We are 'lived' by unknown and uncontrollable forces," Freud wrote, and he went on to say of the conscious ego, "Thus in its relation to the id it is like a man on horse-back, who has to hold in check the superior strength of the horse."[13]

The primary role of human consciousness only *appears* to be the gaining of knowledge of the external world, whereas in essence, according to Freud, it carries on a never-ending and always losing struggle with the sex and death instincts and the repressions based on them. The price of civilization, with its injunctions against fulfillment of the sex and death instincts, leading inevitably to repressions, is neurosis. As a result, everybody is more or less neurotic.

Under the influence of his own speculations Freud himself became more and more deeply cynical. He finally reached the point where he could say: "I can at any rate listen without taking umbrage to those critics who aver that when one surveys the aims of civilization and the means it employs, one is bound to conclude that the whole thing is not worth the effort and that in the end it can only produce a state of things which no individual will be able to bear. . . . My courage fails me, therefore, at the thought of rising up as a prophet before my fellow-men, and I bow to their reproach that I have no consolation to offer them."[14] The faith of the scientist in the power of knowledge was by now wholly transformed into cynicism.

In the meantime, a seminar led by Freud had become the Vienna Psychoanalytical Society, and a second society had been formed in Zurich, Switzerland, under the leadership of C. G. Jung. As Freud put it, "The result of the official anathema against psycho-analysis was that the analysts began to come closer together."[15] Since scientific, medical and academic circles treated them with scorn and derision, they formed their own associations.

In 1908, the Vienna and Zurich societies, together with followers from other countries, including A. A. Brill of New York, met in Salzburg for what in fact if not in name was the inaugural International Psychoanalytical Congress, the first of a long line of annual congresses extending, except for war years, down to the present. A result of this first congress was the founding of a psychoanalytical yearbook which served Freud as a ready-made means of publishing.

About this time Brill undertook to translate Freud's works into English and thus introduce psychoanalysis into the United States. Freud himself visited America in 1909 at the invitation of G. Stanley Hall, the president of Clark University, and gave a course of five lectures attended by leading academic psychologists, clinicians and neurologists. For the first time, Freud became "respectable." A leading professor at Harvard, J. J. Putnam, championed his cause and his career in America was off to an auspicious start. From the very outset psychoanalysis, in spite of bitter opposition, found a "home" in the United States.

Following the First World War the psychoanalytic movement became world-wide, with a vast outpouring of literature. Freud's teachings broke far beyond the boundaries of psychology and psycho-pathology, and in fact became an all-embracing philosophy of life. In a series of books and papers Freud applied his theory of repression, "by a bold extension," as he put it, "to the human race as a whole."[16] Chief among the books were: *Leonardo da Vinci, A Study in Psychosexuality* (1910); *Totem and Taboo* (1913); and *Moses and Monotheism* (1939). In these volumes and in a number of shorter pieces, he outlined the implications of psychoanalysis for many fields of human understanding. He dealt with such subjects as the origins of society, morality and religion, the theory of history, of the nation, of art, of the cause and nature of war, and many others. Here we can only indicate briefly the general character of his efforts in some of these fields.

Freud devoted two books, *Totem and Taboo* and *Moses and Monotheism,* to expounding the psychoanalytic theory of the origins of society, morality and religion. He based his convictions on whatever ethnical theories seemed to suit his purposes, even though they had more recently come into disrepute among ethnologists. In defense of this practice he wrote: "Above all, however, I am not an ethnologist, but a psychoanalyst. It was my good right to select from ethnological data what would serve me for my analytic work."[17] Borrowing whatever he could use, he constructed his theory of social, moral and religious origins.

He advances a hypothesis which may seem fantastic but which offers the advantage of establishing an unsuspected correlation between groups of phenomena that have hitherto been disconnected. He begins with the notion that man originally lived in a "primal horde" organized as a patriarchy. "All that we find there is a violent and jealous father who keeps all the females for himself and drives away his sons as they grow up. . . . One day the brothers who had been driven out came together, killed and devoured their father and so made an end of the patriarchal horde. . . . Cannibal savages as they were, it goes without saying that they devoured their victim as well as killing him. . . . The totem meal, which is perhaps mankind's earliest festival, would thus be a repetition and a commemoration of this memorable and criminal deed, which was the beginning of so many things — of social organization, of moral restrictions, and of religion."[18]

"In the beginning was the deed," Freud quoted from Goethe, but it was a dastardly deed of patricide. The murder of the patriarchal father led, according to Freud, to the establishment of society on the basis of a peculiar social contract; the sons, all half-brothers, realized that the fate of the father would inevitably descend on the sons unless they formed a mutual pact prohibiting murder and marriage within the clan. Thus social organization, Freud held, was founded on two moral restrictions following the deed of patricide. Morality and society were viewed as being the result of father-murder and incest.

Behind this theory lay Freud's view of individual development of the male sex. Little boys, infants in fact, fall in love with their mothers and hate, but at the same time revere, their fathers. The father is a rival of the son for the mother's love. This is the famous Freudian "Oedipus complex." The result is that the son wishes his father dead, but represses the wish which then enters The Unconscious retaining its full "charge of psychic energy." The future of the boy depends in large part on how successfully he can divert the energy of the unconscious incestuous and death-wishes toward socially acceptable ends. In any case the wishes force their way into consciousness as more or less camouflaged guilt, in dreams if not in neuroses.

Freud accounts for religion as the mass sense of guilt arising out of the prehistoric deed of patricide. The murdered primal father is later reinstated as God and "original sin" is the memory of the murder of the God-Father. The totemic feast and the Christian communion are the ritualistic reenactment of the murder and the devouring of the primal father. Freud calls this "the scientific myth of the father of the primal horde."

"Society," Freud wrote, "was now based on complicity in the common crime; religion was based on the sense of guilt and the remorse attaching to it; while morality was based partly on the exigencies of this society and partly on the penance demanded by the sense of guilt."

The Oedipus complex, man's relation to his parents, is, for Freud, the source of society, morality and religion. Their origin and development have nothing to do with the labor process nor with the relations people enter into based on the way they obtain food, clothing and shelter. "The beginnings of religion, morals and society converge," Freud insists, "in the Oedipus complex."

In his application of psychoanalysis to "the human race," Freud assumed the existence of "a collective mind in which mental processes occur just as they do in the mind of an individual."[19] Thus the sense of guilt arising from the murder of the primal father has been operative as a powerfully charged "race-memory" for many thousands of years. This sense of guilt exists in each individual of each generation as an hereditary, repressed memory located in The Unconscious. In the individual, from time immemorial and down to the present, the roots of infantile sexuality and the Oedipus complex are inborn, the innate but repressed memory of the original deed of incest, patricide, cannibalism and sadistic cruelty.

According to Freud, then, the character of both the human race and the individual human being is largely formed as the result of the Oedipus complex. Not only society, morality and religion arise in this complex, but history too is moved by it. The Oedipus complex is the motive force of history, for Freud.

History moves essentially as the result of the influence of great men, Freud maintained, and the reason these great men could exert such tremendous influence was because the masses need to submit to the authority of a father-substitute. "Why the great man should rise to significance at all we have no doubt whatever. We know that the great majority of people have a strong need for authority which they can admire, to which they can submit, and which dominates and sometimes even ill-treats them. We have learned from the psychology of the individual whence comes this need of the masses. It is the longing for the father that lives in each of us from his childhood days, for the same father whom the hero of legend boasts of having overcome. And now it begins to dawn on us that all the features with which we furnish the great man are traits of the father, that in this similarity lies the essence, which so far has eluded us, of the great man. . . He must be admired, he may be trusted, but one cannot help also being afraid of him."[20]

Freud repudiates all progress in the science of history and reinstates the "great-man" theory as an inevitable result of the Oedipus complex in mankind and in the individual. There is, according to him, no escape from this theory of history since it is built into the supposed structure of man's inborn mental apparatus.

In an open letter to Albert Einstein written in 1932 at the request of the latter for the purpose of furthering peace, Freud says of war, "it seems quite a natural thing, no doubt it has a good biological basis and in practice it is scarcely avoidable."[21] He goes on to give war an additional basis, a psychological one, in the form of an inborn aggressive, destructive instinct, the death instinct. It is this instinct which has produced wars and inquisitions in the past and which makes war in the future "scarcely avoidable." He speaks in the letter of "an instinct for hatred and destruction which goes halfway to meet the efforts of the war mongers."

Freud outlined his theory of instincts to Einstein: "According to our hypothesis human instincts are of only two kinds: those which seek to preserve and unite . . . and those which seek to destroy and kill and which we class together as the aggressive or destructive instinct. . . . As a result of a little speculation we have come to suppose that this (latter) instinct is at work in every living being and is striving to bring it to ruin and to reduce life to its original condition of inanimate matter. Thus it quite seriously deserves to be called a death instinct." After relating what he calls "our mythological theory of instincts," he evidently felt a little abashed considering to whom he was addressing his remarks, so he hurried on to say to Einstein: "It may perhaps seem to you as though our theories are a kind of mythology and, in the present case, not even an agreeable one. But does not every science come in the end to a kind of mythology like this? Cannot the same be said today of your own Physics?" Since all sciences are held to be mythologies, Freud is pardoned in his own eyes for constructing a mythological psychology in apology for war. It is not the structure of society at certain stages and under certain conditions that leads to war; it is rather the instincts of man, and particularly of the "uncultured masses."

Freud, himself, was opposed to war and considered himself a pacifist. The trouble is that there are not enough pacifists, he says, and there is a good reason why they are so few in number. A pacifist, Freud maintains in the Einstein letter, is one who has renounced instinctual gratifications and impulses and has substituted cultural aims. But the masses, he insists, still are uncultured and still operate on the basis of their instincts and thus are propelled to meet the warmongers half-way. "The ideal condition of things," Freud writes, "would of course be a community of men who had subordinated their instinctual life to the dictatorship of reason . . . but in all probability that is a Utopian expectation. . . . An unpleasant picture comes to one's mind of mills that grind so slowly that people may starve before they get their flour." [22]

Second only to his apology for war is Freud's rationale for the doctrine of female inferiority and male superiority. Instead of tracing the position of women to the conditions existing in certain stages of society, he attributes it to recognition on the part of both sexes of an alleged anatomical "deficiency" in women. Young girls, he holds, assign the lack of the male anatomy to castration as punishment for sin and, if they are to progress normally into "femininity," they must accept an inferior and passive condition. Freud speaks of "the psychological consequences of the anatomical distinction between the sexes" and points to "character-traits which critics of every epoch have brought up against women—that they show less sense of justice than men, that they are less ready to submit to the great necessities of life, that they are more often influenced in their judgments by feelings of affection or hostility." Here again Freud feels a little on the defensive and so hastens to add: "We must not allow ourselves to be deflected from such conclusions by the denials of the feminists, who are anxious to force us to regard the two sexes as completely equal in position and worth."[23]

Freud made what he called a "pathographic elaboration" of Leonardo da Vinci in which he accounted psychoanalytically for the fact that Leonardo was both an artist and a scientist. He was an artist because of the particular form of the Oedipus complex in his case. He was a fatherless child who was in love with his mother, who prematurely awakened his sexual activity the energy of which was then sublimated into activity as an artist. He was a scientist because as a child his sexual activity was concentrated on "investigation" of sexual matters which, being repressed, returned in later life as an obsessive passion for investigating nature.

Art, science and culture in general, were accounted for by Freud in terms of repression of instinctive life and subsequent more or less successful transformation of sexual energy into intellectually creative works. Objective evaluation and criticism of art give place to such pathographic analyses as he made of Leonardo.

Freud's speculations came to an end only with his death. Forty years old when he "discovered" psychoanalysis, he spent forty-three more years first in elaborating it and then in developing his metapsychology and in applying it to "the human race." He had lived in the Vienna Ghetto of Leopoldstadt ever since the age of four, first in poverty but then in relative middle class comfort. In later years he no longer took many patients but devoted his time to writing and to the training of analysts. The last fifteen years of his life he had suffered from cancer of the mouth, kept from his throat only by repeated operations.

In 1938, when death was closing in, the Nazis invaded Austria and soon had confiscated all Freud's possessions, his publishing house, his library and his fortune. Most serious of all, his passport was taken away. He was now a prisoner of Hitler in the Ghetto. The International Psychoanalytic movement brought pressure to bear for his freedom. A ransom was demanded and one of his patients and followers, Princess Marie Bonaparte, paid one-quarter of a million schillings for his release. The Freud family travelled to England where the final year of his life was spent. Four of his sisters, remaining in Vienna, were murdered in the Nazi gas chambers. On September 23, 1939, Freud died.

The preceding is a highly compressed life-story of Sigmund Freud demonstrating that the eighty-three years of his life were divided between two contrasting careers, as physiologist-neurologist and as psychoanalyst. The dedication to natural science and the established scientific method characteristic of the first half of Freud's life sharply confronts the conjectures and speculations of the second half. From the careful scientific worker, satisfied with slow but verified advances in knowledge, he became, *at least in part,* an impatient adventurer, satisfied only with bold and sweeping solutions to age-old problems. He became, that is, a metaphysician, in his own words a "metapsychologist," literally a maker-of-myths.

At the same time, psychoanalysis is without question founded on *observation* of patients. The basic working theories of the unconscious, repression, sublimation, regression, fixation and the like are said to be the outcome of practical experience and to be thus independent and separable from the metapsychological speculations. The claim is made that Freud the psychoanalyst founded a new science, the science of unconscious mental life, based on his work with his patients, and that this science does not require the web of myths. The latter is according to this view simply an attempt to "round out" a complete psychological-philosophical system.

The first question to be investigated, then, is: Are the working theories of psychoanalysis independent of the speculative system, or are they, on the contrary, dependent on and inextricably intermeshed with it. In short, are the myths an essential part of psychoanalysis or are they not?

A second question concerns more directly the confrontation of the early and late Freud. It may be that the confrontation itself is inadmissable because of the qualitatively different subject-matters involved. It is generally considered to be one thing to investigate natural phenomena such as the nervous system and the brain by the methods of science, and quite another thing to make a study of the human mind. Perhaps the established scientific procedures can be employed on the former but are useless with regard to the latter. Some form of introspective, subjective analysis of the psyche *may* be the only means of investigating so complex a phenomenon. The sharp contrast between the early and late Freud may simply reflect the contrast between material and mental processes.

The second question, then, is: Can mental activity be investigated by means of the established scientific methods employed to gain knowledge of other natural phenomena, or must an exception be granted in this case? The intra-Freud confrontation cannot furnish the answer. Psychoanalysis must be confronted by an attempt to apply the objective experimental methods of natural science specifically to the higher parts of the brain as the organ of psychic life. Pavlov's science of higher nervous activity meets this requirements, and therefore a confrontation of Freud and Pavlov should furnish an answer.

The remainder of this book is concerned primarily with the two questions. Thus it proceeds on two levels: (1) an investigation of psychoanalysis itself to determine whether Freud's working theories do or do not require the myth-making speculative system: on the outcome of this investigation hinges the validity and credibility of the theories; and (2) a confrontation of Freud by Pavlov to determine whether or not the objective methods of science are applicable to mental life.

In the process of finding answers to these questions, we should approach the solution to the over-all problem: Which of the two approaches is more valid, more scientific, more effective, and which therefore holds out the better promise of helping man to know himself in health and in illness?

The first step is to examine the contrasting methods employed by Pavlov and Freud.

Chapter II

THE INTERPRETATION OF DREAMS AND THE SALIVARY REFLEX

IN THE COURSE of their respective work, Pavlov and Freud came upon certain unexpected phenomena which set each off in search of the solution to the riddle of the sphinx, the nature of human nature. Pavlov in his experiments on the digestive glands and Freud in his practice as a private neurologist were confronted with turning points in their careers. The stories are here briefly related in close juxtaposition.

Pavlov's experiments on the nervous regulation of the digestive glands had, for years prior to 1900, been consistently disrupted by occurrences beyond the scope of the experimental situation. He had been primarily concerned with the secretion of digestive juices when diverse foods were introduced into the mouths of his laboratory animals. But even before any food was put into the mouth, it was found that there was already set in motion an ample flow of glandular secretions. As soon as the animal smelt or saw the food being prepared, or heard the footsteps of the person doing the feeding, the digestive juices began to flow. Pavlov ignored this interference with his experiments as long as possible, but finally had to face the problem. The phenomenon was in fact analogous to the familiar one of "mouth watering" at the sight or scent of food. Such *action-at-a-distance* had heretofore been considered the exclusive subject-matter of psychology, and had been dealt with in the purely descriptive terms of the conscious life of human beings.

Pavlov was now determined to investigate action-at-a-distance, through eyes, ears and nose, by the strictly objective experimental method employed in the science of physiology. The first problem was how to go about such an investigation. He was convinced of only one thing, that the activity in question could not be understood in terms of human consciousness with its categories of thought, judgment and will. Some experimental method had to be found which would make possible the examination of the phenomena without recourse to probing the non-existent human consciousness of animals. His problem, then, was to find a means of investigating the *unconscious* behavior of dogs, apes and other mammals. He had to find or construct a *fistula, or window, which would allow him to observe the functioning of the unconscious activity of the nervous system, and particularly of its apex, the brain.*

Freud, after years of training in neuro-anatomy, medicine and neurology, had finally established himself in private practice as a neurologist. He was faced with a practical problem: how to treat the neurotics who formed by far the majority of his patients. He tried all the remedies in the textbooks and some which were not yet included. Among the latter, one in particular, hypnotic suggestion, at first produced startling results. But in the course of using hypnotic suggestion as a therapeutic measure, Freud came upon certain intrusive phenomena which were not anticipated in the therapeutic situation. He found that under hypnosis the patient could recall memories, impulses and emotions which were not at all within the scope of conscious recall. Further he found that, in the case of certain memories, there was powerful *resistance* on the part of the patient, when awakened from hypnosis, to admitting the forgotten memory to consciousness. He found in short that there was a part of the mind that worked *unconsciously*. This submerged part of mental life continually disrupted his attempted cures of his patients' ailments and finally, in 1895, he determined to investigate what he called *unconscious mental activity*. The problem was *how?* Some method was required which would make possible the probing of *unconscious* memories, wishes, resistances and their like. Of one thing Freud was certain, probing of the *consciousness* of his patients coud not serve his purposes. He had to find a method of discovering thoughts, memories, wishes and resistances which somehow operated below the level of consciousness. He had to find a *fistula, or window, through which he could observe the functioning of unconscious mental activity.*

The first step, then, for both Pavlov and Freud in their search for the key to understanding psychic life was to find some fistula which would allow them to investigate unconscious activity. But here the paths begin to diverge. On the one hand, Pavlov required a literal, physiological fistula facing on unconscious nervous and particularly *cerebral* activity, while on the other hand Freud needed a figurative, psychological fistula facing on unconscious *mental* activity.

The Salivary Fistula and the Dream Fistula

Among several possible alternatives, Pavlov selected the salivary gland as best suited for his experimental purposes. This gland is located in the mouth, at the entrance to the digestive tract of the animal organism and is connected, functionally, with both the external world and the internal life of the animal. Its advantages as a subject for experimentation lie in its accessibility, its relative simplicity and, most important, in the fact that its secretions can be measured quantitatively and analyzed qualitatively.

Choosing dogs as experimental animals, Pavlov surgically constructed a fistula directly into the salivary gland, inserted a small duct and attached a test-tube to the outer end. In his way, when the gland was set in motion by one or another stimulus, saliva was secreted not into the dog's mouth but into the test-tube. The experimenter could then measure the amount of saliva secreted and analyze it chemically to determine its composition. The theory on which this experimental technique was based was the long established one that the nervous system functions by means of reflexes. A stimulus from the external world sets in motion a particular muscle or gland which then performs its given task. The particular task of the salivary gland is, among others, to "lubricate" food that has been introduced into the mouth, and thus facilitate the process of swallowing.

Thus Pavlov constructed a fistula which allowed him to study the reflex activity of the salivary gland, and through such study, to discover facts and laws of reflex activity in general, especially the reflex mechanism of what he tentatively called "psychic phenomena" or action-at-a-distance through the sense organs. His immediate goal was to investigate the nervous activity underlying animal behavior. His ultimate aim was to find out how the nervous system, and in the first place, the brain, forms the basis of man's mental life and of human nature as a whole.

Freud required some method of penetrating below the level of consciousness. He had to find phenomena which were mental and yet at the same time were not conscious. Such phenomena could then serve as the required "fistula" yielding access to unconscious mental life. In due time he found several types of phenomena that met the requirement. There was one, however, which he rated far above the others, namely *dreams*. Dreams, he maintained, are mental phenomena and yet, being characteristic of sleep, are not part of conscious life. He became convinced that by probing, analyzing and interpreting dreams, unconscious mental processes could be examined and their facts and laws discovered. The interpretation of dreams constitutes Freud's chief "fistula" for the investigation of man's unconscious psyche. That he viewed dream-interpretation explicitly as a fistula is indicated when, in speaking of the unconscious "structure of the psychic apparatus," he says, "By means of dream-interpretation we are able to glance as through an inspection-hole into the interior of this apparatus." [1]

In addition to the interpretation of dreams, Freud employed a number of other fistula-inspection-holes giving access to unconscious mental activity, including free association, transference phenomena, neurotic symptoms, hypnotic suggestion, errors and jokes. The theory on which all these investigative techniques are based is that, according to Freud, consciousness tends to prevent unconscious material from manifesting itself and must somehow be circumvented, or "caught off guard." All the "fistulas" employed by Freud are designed to evade the watchful eye of conscious life, and thereby allow unconscious memories, ideas, emotions, wishes and impulses to indicate their presence, however indirectly.

Thus both Pavlov and Freud succeeded, to their own satisfaction at least, in their respective quests for a fistula giving access to unconscious activity: Pavlov found his in the tapping of the salivary gland as a means of investigating unconscious *nervous,* and particularly *cerebral,* activity; while Freud found his in (among others) the interpretation of dreams as a means of investigating unconscious *mental* processes.

Pavlov's Salivary Fistula In Operation

Pavlov's specific problem was how to study the psychical or signalling activity of the cerebral hemispheres. Any reflex could have been chosen since signalling stimuli are connected with all reflexes. But for experimental convenience he selected two relatively simple ones connected with the mouth: The alimentary or feeding reflex manifested when food is put in the mouth; and the mild-defensive reflex manifested when an unpalatable substance is introduced into the mouth. Both are normal and ordinary phenomena, observable every day in animals and in ourselves. The alimentary and mild-defensive reflexes of the mouth have another and decisive advantage for laboratory investigation. They each have two aspects, muscular action and glandular action. The alimentary reflex, when stimulated by food in the mouth, consists on the one hand in chewing and swallowing, and on the other in immediate secretion of saliva needed for the physical and chemical processes of digestion. The mild-defensive reflex, when stimulated by an unpalatable substance, consists on the one hand in spitting and on the other in secretion of saliva needed for cleansing the mouth. In each of the two mouth-reflexes analysis, quantitative and qualitative, would be exceedingly difficult with the muscular activity, but very simple with the secretory response. Saliva can easily be measured as to intensity of flow by counting drops, and quality of composition by chemical analysis. Thus Pavlov used the salivary component of the alimentary and mild-defensive reflexes exclusively in his experiments.

In addition to the fact that measuring and analyzing muscular responses would require the most delicate instruments and even then would not give the precision that is achieved in the case of salivary secretion, Pavlov characteristically pointed to another advantage of concentrating his experiments on the salivary gland: "Of certain importance in the early phase of our work was the fact that during observations on the secretion of saliva there was a lesser tendency towards anthropomorphic interpretations than was the case during observations of the motor reactions."[2] Along the same lines, he established in his laboratory a strict system of fines to be levied against himself and his assistants for each lapse into interpreting animal behavior in terms of human conscious activity—feeling, desiring, thinking, judging and their like. Above all, he was concerned with making a thoroughly *objective*, as opposed to a subjective, introspective study of the psychic or signalling activity of the cerebral hemispheres.

To study cerebral signalling activity as manifested in the secretion of saliva, the dogs used in the experiments were subjected to a minor operation performed under hospital aseptic conditions, for above all the animals had to return to good health and normal behavior before they could be used in the laboratory. The opening of the salivary duct was surgically transplanted to the external surface of the jowl. As a result, the saliva flowed not into the mouth but out the cheek. A glass tube attached to the duct made it possible either to count the drops by an automatic electrical device, or to measure the flow in a graduated tube.

Since the cerebral hemispheres are a highly complex signalling apparatus sensitive to a myriad of diverse, colliding and interacting stimuli from the environment, it was absolutely essential to take elaborate precautions against these influences. All of them acting at once would be chaotic and would make it impossible to carry on experimental work. The conditions therefore had to be greatly simplified. A special laboratory was built, at the expense of an enlightened Moscow businessman, at the Institute of Experimental Medicine. The main task was to eliminate as far as possible all stimuli which were not part of the experimental situation. For this purpose each research room was divided into two sound-proof compartments, one for the animal and one for the experimenter. Pneumatic or electric transmission was used by the experimenter, from a control board in his compartment, for applying the various stimuli to the dog. The control panel was of necessity highly complex since a great variety of stimuli were required to investigate the tremendously wide range of the intricate cerebral signalling apparatus.

Here is a simple demonstration of the salivary fistula in operation as an experimental technique for the investigation of the unconscious signalling activity of the cerebral cortex.

"*Demonstration.* Food is shown to the animal. As you see, the secretion of saliva begins after five seconds, and in fifteen seconds six drops of saliva have been collected. . . .

"This is also a case of signalling due to the activity of the cerebral hemispheres; it has been acquired in the course of the animal's individual existence and is by no means an inborn reaction. . . . Consequently, the sight of food does not, in itself, evoke a salivary reaction, and does not represent an inborn agent of this reaction. Only after the pups had had several meals of meat and bread did the sight of these items produce a salivary secretion."

On the basis of such experiments, Pavlov poses his central problem, "Now comes the fundamental question: What is the nature of signalization and how should it be considered from the purely physiological point of view?"[3] His answer was found, of course, in further experiments: The *conditioned reflex,* with its facts and laws of functioning.

Such is Pavlov's salivary fistula in operation; now we turn our attention to Freud's dream-fistula.

Freud's Dream-Fistula in Operation

Freud's specific problem was how to study the unconscious processes of mental activity. He came upon the solution almost by accident in the course of treating his ambulatory neurotic patients. "In the course of these psycho-analytic studies," he relates, "I happened upon the question of dream-interpretation. My patients, after I had pledged them to inform me of all the ideas and thoughts which occurred to them in connection with a given theme, related their dreams, and thus taught me that a dream may be interpolated in the psychic concatenation." He became convinced that dreams have meaning and that the interpretation of dreams is possible. "I have been forced to perceive," he says, "that here, once more, we have one of those cases where an ancient and stubbornly retained popular belief seems to have come nearer to the truth of the matter than the opinion of modern science. I must insist that the dream actually does possess a meaning, and that a scientific method of dream-interpretation is possible."

In what does Freud's "scientific interpretation of dreams" consist? In the first place, "a certain psychic preparation of the patient is necessary." He must be impressed with the importance of sharpening his own psychic perceptions, that is, he must pay attention to all ideas, feelings, thoughts, and impulses which may come to mind without censoring or dismissing any of them as indecent, painful, embarrassing, or unimportant. "He must be explicitly instructed," Freud says, "to renounce all criticism of the thought-formations which he may perceive. . . . He must preserve an absolute impartiality in respect of his ideas; for if he is unsuccessful in finding the desired solution of the dream, it will be because he permits himself to be critical of them." The first condition, then, for a scientific interpretation of dreams is self-observation in the form of free or involuntary association without critical interference from one's conscious mind.

Conscious mind, in the course of rational thought, either in communication with one's self or with others, must of necessity exercise a maximum of critical interference designed to eliminate irrelevant ideas. For the purposes of dream interpretation, however, Freud insists on the opposite procedure: "In self-observation, on the other hand, he (the patient) has but one task, that of suppressing criticism; if he succeeds in doing this an unlimited number of thoughts enter his consciousness which would otherwise have eluded his grasp. With the aid of the material thus obtained, material which is new to the self-observer, it is possible to achieve the interpretation of dream formations." For the interpretation of dreams it is necessary to suppress rational thought, and "to induce a psychic state which is in some degree analogous to the state of the mind before falling asleep, and also, of course, to the hypnotic state." In such a state, "undesired ideas emerge, owing to the slackening of a certain arbitrary, and, of course, critical action which is allowed to influence the trend of our ideas. . . . In the condition which is utilized for the analysis of dreams, this (critical) activity is purposely and deliberately renounced, and the psychic energy thus saved (or some part of it) is employed in attentively tracking the undesired thoughts which now come to the surface." The free association of undesired thoughts evokes the most violent resistance which seeks to prevent them from coming to consciousness. Thus the suspension of rational, critical thought has as its purpose the circumventing of this resistance. To achieve this semi-soporific, unrational state of self-observation or introspection, "the patient should take up a restful position and close his eyes."[4]

The patient is now asked to relate his dream. The latter is treated, not as a whole, but as a "comglomerate of psychic formations." The details of the dream are taken separately and analyzed for meanings. As an aid in the search for the meaning of the various parts of the dream, the patient is requested to let his mind play over each one without critical attention. This is the process of freely associating described above. As a result of the dream and the free-associations about its separate elements, the analyst has at hand a number of images, visual and auditory. The next step is to interpret the images. This is done primarily by means of a set of stereotyped symbols with their previously established meaning, what Freud calls "symbol-translation."[5] "We arrive in this way," he says, "at constant translations for a series of dream-elements, just as in popular books on dreams we find such translations for everything that occurs in dreams. ... We call a constant relation of this kind between a dream element and its translation a *symbolic* one, and the dream element itself a *symbol* of the Unconscious dream-thought. Freud insists that "the relation between a symbol and the idea symbolized is an invariable one."[6] It is primarily this constant and invariable character of symbol-translation which makes possible the interpretation of dreams. In certain cases, according to Freud, when the personality, life conditions and recent experience of the patient are known to the analyst, dreams can be interpreted without questioning the dreamer, solely by translating the symbols.

Most of the symbols in dreams are sexual in character. "An overwhelming majority of symbols in dreams," Freud says, "are sexual symbols."[7] This largely accounts for the fact that the ideas and impulses they represent are *undesired*. When they are interpreted as sexual symbols representing genitalia, intercourse and perversions, it gives universal offense to dreamers.

Freud's chief fistula or "inspection-hole" on unconscious mental processes is, then, the dream and its interpretation, primarily through symbol translation. That symbol-translation is decisive in the interpretation of dreams is indicated when Freud remarks "how impossible it is to arrive at the interpretation of a dream if one excludes dream symbolism." [8]

Now we are ready to witness Freud's fistula, the interpretation of dreams, at work in the task of revealing how unconscious mental processes operate. The following is taken from one of his case studies:

> The hat as the symbol of a man (of the male genitals): (A fragment from the dream of a young woman who suffered from agoraphobia as the result of her fear of temptation.)
>
> "*I am walking in the street in summer; I am wearing a straw hat of peculiar shape, the middle piece of which is bent upwards, while the side pieces hang downwards (here the description hesitates), and in such a fashion that one hangs lower than the other. I am cheerful and in a confident mood, and as I pass a number of young officers I think to myself: You can't do anything to me.*"
>
> As she could produce no associations to the hat, I said to her: "The hat is really a male genital organ, with its raised middle piece and the two downward-hanging side pieces." It is perhaps peculiar that her hat should be supposed to be a man, but after all one says: *Unter die Haube kommen* (to get under the cap) when we mean: to get married. I intentionally refrained from interpreting the details concerning the unequal dependence of the two side pieces, although the determination of just such details must point the way to the interpretation. I went on to say that if, therefore, she had a husband with such splendid genitals she would not have to fear the officers; that is, she would have nothing to wish from them, for it was essentially her temptation-phantasies which prevented her from going about unprotected and unaccompanied. This last explanation of her anxiety I had already been able to give her repeatedly on the basis of other material.
>
> It is quite remarkable how the dreamer behaved after this interpretation. She withdrew her description of the hat, and would not admit that she had said that the two side pieces were hanging down. I was, however, too sure of what I had heard to allow myself to be misled, and so I insisted that she did say it. She was quiet for a while, and then found the courage to ask why it was that one of her husband's testicles was lower than the other, and whether it was the same with all men. With this the peculiar detail of the hat was explained, and the whole interpretation was accepted by her.
>
> The hat symbol was familiar to me long before the patient related this dream. From other but less transparent cases I believed that I might assume the hat could also stand for the female genitals.[10]

By means of such interpretations of dreams, Freud proposed to discover the functioning of the unconscious mental apparatus.

What he found through the fistula of dream interpretation, with its free association and symbol-translation, we will see in the following chapter. We are concerned here, however, with comparing the fistulas and investigative techniques employed by Freud and Pavlov.

Perhaps the most striking impression is that Freud's approach is primarily *introspective* or *subjective, while Pavlov's* is essentially *objective.* Freud's procedure is based largely on self-observation and the observation of self-observation. Of necessity there can be no witnesses of dream interpretation, nor are the interpretations repeatable, except in the most general way. Even the verification of Freud's hypotheses, as he himself testifies, is possible primarily by submission of oneself to psychoanalysis, either to self-analysis or analysis at the hands of a trained analyst.

"Now you will have a right," he says, "to ask the question: If no objective evidence for psychoanalysis exists and no possibility of demonstrating the process, how is it possible to study it at all or to convince oneself of its truth? The study of it is indeed not an easy matter, nor are there many people who have thoroughly learned it; still there is, of course, some way of learning it. Psychoanalysis is learned first of all on oneself, through the study of one's own personality. This is not exactly what is meant by introspection, but it may be so described for want of a better word. There is a whole series of very common and well-known mental phenomena which can be taken as material for self-analysis when one has acquired some knowledge of the method. In this way one may obtain the required conviction of the reality of the processes which psychoanalysis describes, and of the truth of its conceptions, although progress on these lines is not without its limitations. One gets much further by submitting oneself to analysis by a skilled analyst, undergoing the working of the analysis in one's own person and using the opportunity to observe the finer details of the technique which the analyst employs. This, eminently the best way, is of course only practicable for individuals."

One cannot witness the process of analysis, nor even eavesdrop on it. "Let us be content," Freud says, "if we may overhear the words which pass between the analyst and the patient. But even that is impossible. The dialogue which constitutes the analysis will admit of no audience; the process cannot be demonstrated. . . . It is impossible, therefore, for you to be actually present during a psychoanalytic treatment; you can only be told about it, and can learn psychoanalysis, in the strictest sense of the word, only by heresay."[11] "The only alternative to hearsay evidence is to submit oneself to analysis. Thus according to Freud, verification of the hypotheses of dream interpretation, and of other elements of his system, can be made in the final instance solely by introspection or case histories of introspection.*

Introspection means looking into one's own mind, inspecting one's own thoughts or feelings. It is the practice of self-examination or self-observation. In psychoanalysis, self-analysis is in the strictest sense introspection. But even an analysis made by a trained analyst on a patient is ultimately dependent on the introspective activity of the latter. Such investigative techniques as dream interpretation and free association depend essentially on the self-observation of the patient. He must relate his dream and report his spontaneous associations. Much depends on his attitude, for if he is uncooperative, reticent, not fully candid, or is outright deceitful in the analytical situation, the entire procedure is put in jeopardy. Further, everything depends on the patient's own selections, judgments, feelings, attitudes, temperament, personal bias, emotional background, and similar *subjective* elements.

Subjective in the sense used here, means dependence on the character of a personal, human subject with all his private emotions, impulses, biases, idiosyncrasies, habits and attitudes. It means determination by the make-up of the individual mind rather than by objective conditions and facts. For example, a *subjective judgment* is one in which personal preference or bias takes precedence over an evaluation made on the basis of objective facts which exist independently of personal preference. *Subjective* means conditioned by personal characteristics.

Freud's investigative method, his psychoanalysis by means of the interpretation of dreams and free association, must be

---

*In recent years there have been numerous attempts to establish certain of Freud's hypotheses by means of experimentation. These attempts are dealt with in a forthcoming book.

characterized as essentially subjective and introspective. In fact, one of the universally accepted features of subjectivism, according to *Webster's Collegiate Dictionary*, is "requiring or exhibiting introspection." The admitted fact that Freud's hypotheses, generalized from case histories of analyses, cannot be demonstrated, but can only be personally undergone or experienced, is weighty evidence, indeed, in support of the contention that his method of investigation is subjective and introspective.

On the other hand, it would be difficult to dispute the contention that Pavlov's investigative method is objective. *Objective* means viewing phenomena as external and apart from self-consciousness. It means to be detached and impersonal. It involves eliminating as far as possible the peculiarly personal element in observation, judgment and investigation. It signifies the status of existing and operating independently of the mind with its personal emotions and biases. It has to do with the object as it is in itself, independent of the conscious or unconscious individual characteristics of the observer or investigator. It is the opposite of subjective.

One of Pavlov's primary concerns in establishing experimental procedure was to eliminate, as far as humanly possible, the subjective factor. It was for this reason, for example, that he selected the salivary secretion rather than the muscular response as the indicator of reflex activity. Muscular response, he maintained, would have to be described verbally by the laboratory technician as a result of visual observation, and this would allow room for expressions of personal preference, the subjective factor. The secretion of saliva, on the other hand, could be measured electrically or in calibrated test-tubes and thus would not require interpretation by the experimenter. Likewise, the lay-out of the laboratory and all the elaborate precautions taken to prevent extraneous stimuli from acting on the dog while in the experimental chamber, were designed to insure the objectivity of the procedure.

In addition, Pavlov's experiments are fully repeatable and many have been repeated innumerable times by scientists throughout the world.* All the facts, laws and hypotheses,

*Among them, the Gantt laboratory at Johns Hopkins, the Liddell laboratory at Cornell, and the Lashly laboratory at the University of Chicago.

generalized by Pavlov, are fully verifiable. They are all subject to objective, experimental investigation, and can be tested by scientists trained in the employment of the universally accepted methods of scientific procedure.

That Pavlov's investigative method is objective is not, however, the main question. Few, if any, would seriously deny it. The real question, one which, at this point, could legitimately be raised by anyone, and which may well have occurred to the reader, concerns the *comparability* of Freud's subjective, introspective method with Pavlov's objective, experimental method, considering the qualitatively different subject-matters on which each is employed. May it not be that Freud's subject-matter, the unconscious mental life of human beings, is wholly unamenable to objective methods of investigation? That the latter may be adapted to the study of the cerebral functioning of dogs, but not to the higher nervous activity underlying the complexities of human nature? Perhaps introspection is the sole means for examining mental phenomena. This is a similar problem to that encountered in the confrontation of Freud's two careers. We note, however, that Pavlov's ultimate aim was to discover the basis of *human* mental life and mental illness by means of the objective investigation of animal and human higher nervous activity. Let us therefore defer judgment on this key question until we have proceeded further with the juxtaposition of Freud's and Pavlov's work, and more particularly until we have compared the results of their respective approaches in the decisive fields of psychology and psychiatry.

Both Pavlov and Freud, by means of their fistulas and investigative procedures, claimed to have made fundamental "discoveries." True or false, these "discoveries" are still today of world-shaking proportions. By means of the salivary fistula and the objective experimental method, Pavlov produced phenomena out of which he constructed *the theory of conditioned reflexes*. By means of the dream fistula, Freud unearthed phenomena out of which he constructed *the theory of repression*. We turn now to an examination and confrontation of these two theories.

Chapter III

THE THEORY OF REPRESSION, PSYCHIC ENERGY AND THE CONDITIONED REFLEX

FROM OBSERVATIONS MADE by means of their fistulas and investigative procedures, Freud and Pavlov amassed a wealth of material which they generalized into their respective theories of repression and of the conditioned reflex. The latter is the central theory in all Pavlov's work on higher nervous activity, and the former, as Freud always maintained, is the "foundation stone" of psychoanalysis. The two theories are here presented one immediately following the other so that their basic elements can be compared and their relative scientific merit judged.

Freud's Theory of Repression

"The doctrine of repression," Freud maintained, "is the outcome of psychoanalytic work, a theoretic inference legitimately drawn from innumerable observations."[1] The observations, from which the theory of repression was inferred, were made by means of the interpretation of dreams with the aid of free association and the meaning of symbols. In case after case, Freud uncovered the following three phenomena: (1) dream analysis and free association revealed that the patient had forgotten many facts of his past life; (2) everything that had been forgotten had in some way or other been painful — either alarming or disagreeable or shameful by the standards of the subject's personality; (3) to bring the patient to remember the forgotten facts of his life it was necessary to overcome something that fought against their recall — it was necessary for the analyst to make an expenditure of effort to compel and subdue it.[2] Such were the observations, repeated hundreds of times, which led Freud to infer the theory of repression.

The starting point for the theory of repression is, then, the commonplace observation of the facts of forgetting and remembering. The first problem, however, arises when the act of remembering has not yet taken place. How can the analyst discover the past and long forgotten experience, thought or impulse when the subject himself not only has not yet recalled it, but does not know anything about it, nor even that it exists? Dream interpretation—free associations on the various elements of the dream and treating the imagery of the dream as symbols with established meanings which can be translated —was Freud's primary solution of the problem. As aids in this process of detection of forgotten material or unconscious memories, he relied on such observable phenomena as symptomatic actions, for example fingering objects or tapping with the fingers during the analysis. Slips of tongue and pen, in fact, errors involving forgetting of whatever kind, were carefully noted. In addition, any developing attitude on the part of the subject directed toward the analyst was closely watched for signs of emotions which might indicate forgotten feelings now transferred to other persons or to the analyst himself.

By means of all these indications, but in the first place by means of the interpretation of dreams, Freud sought to discover the unconscious forgotten material stored in the lower depths of the mind.

The theory of repression is an hypothesis to account for the subject's tenacious opposition to remembering those long-forgotten painful experiences which the analyst had already disclosed, by means of dream-symbol translation, as existing deep in his unconscious mind. Just as the interpretation of dreams is the basis of the *method* of psychoanalysis, the theory of repression as Freud said, is "the foundation-stone on which the whole structure of psychoanalysis rests."[3] We present the theory of repression first in its simplest, unelaborated form.

The mechanism of repression of ideas or impulses leading to forgetting is, according to Freud, the following. A particular *impulsion* had at one time arisen in the subject's mind but was immediately opposed by other *powerful tendencies* on the grounds that it was shameful. After a more or less extended conflict between the two, the shameful impulse had been rejected and forced out of consciousness. This impuse, however, had not thereupon simply dissipated, but had remained in another part of the mind as an unconscious impulsion retaining its original force. The force of the impulse insistently demanded reentry into consciousness, but was continually blocked by the vigilance of the latter. The forceful impulse would not be denied. Since it could not gain entrance to consciousness by direct means, it resorted to indirect, devious methods. By circuitous routes, the impulse enters consciousness time after time, but in a multitude of disguised forms. Such is the bare skeleton of the theory of repression.[4]

The first task of analysis is twofold; to identify the disguised forms and to penetrate through the disguise to uncover the originally repressed and long-forgotten impulse. The second task, also twofold, is to bring the subject to remember the formerly conscious impulse and in so doing to overcome his more or less strong reluctance to remember that which he had once repressed and forgotten.

Freud's development of psychoanalysis can be viewed for the most part as a continuous elaboration, ended only by his death, of the theory of repression as outlined above. We will see much more of this elaboration in the following chapters. Here, however, we are concerned with its most fundamental elements.

In the essential elaboration of the theory, the shameful *impulse* was said to be a mental representation of one or another of the *instincts,* particularly of the *sexual instinct*. When some impulse or idea representing, for example, the sexual instinct enters consciousness it is met by other powerful *tendencies* in the form of the subject's *conscience*. The conscience, embodying the social norms, moral standards, ethical ideals and religious beliefs of the subject's personality, judges the impulse or idea to be shameful and therefore painful, and at once enters into conflict with it. After a sharp struggle, the shameful instinct-presentation is ejected from consciousness. The conscience thus acts as a *censor* screening what may or may not remain in consciousness. But conscience has an additional task. Not only does it eject unwanted instinct presentations, but it acts as guardian standing at the gates of consciousness to prevent *reentry* of the ejected impulses and ideas. Thus conscience is the active agent of repression proper, and the latter consists of two processes; the ejection and the debarring of shameful material from consciousness.

When a shameful instinct presentation is repressed it returns to the abode of all repressed ideas which Freud now calls *The Unconscious*. The Unconscious is a mental repository, located somewhere in the mind, not only for repressed material but for all instinct presentations whether or not they have ever entered consciousness. An instinct presentation is, according to Freud, an idea or an impulse expressing a biological instinct.

The repressed instinct presentation, on returning to The Unconscious, retains its force or power of expressing itself in emotions or in motor activity. This retained force is now, in the elaborated theory, called by Freud a *charge of psychic energy* or a *cathexis*. All instinct presentations, whether they remain in The Unconscious, or enter consciousness, or are repressed back into The Unconscious, retain their charges of psychic energy, their cathexis. After repression a cathected idea or impulse restlessly and ceaselessly seeks reentry into consciousness, or discharge in the motor activity of behavior.

The disguised forms assumed by cathected instinct-presentations are found as elements in *dreams;* as relatively unguarded *free associations;* as *slips of tongue and pen;* as *symptomatic actions; as transferred emotions and attitudes;* as socially acceptable *substitute gratifications,* called *sublimations,* including intellectual, artistic, political, moral or religious pursuits; as relatively unguarded *wit and humor;* and finally, in psychopathological cases, as *neurotic* and *psychotic symptoms* including fantasies and delusions.[5]

In this elaborated form of the theory of repression, the task of the analyst becomes still more evident. If he is to discover the subject's repressed impulses, long forgotten and unconscious, he must carefully observe his dreams, his free associations, his slips of tongue and pen, his symptomatic actions, his transferred emotions and attitudes, his sublimations, his wit and humor, and, if the subject be a patient, the analyst must carefully observe the subjective content of his fantasies or delusions. The psychoanalyst must search all such phenomena for those disguised forms of expression which might indicate the nature of the original cathected instinct-presentation which had, sometime in the patient's life, been repressed.

Once he has discovered, or thinks he has discovered, the original repressed instinct-presentation, he must overcome the opposition of the subject to recalling it to consciousness. In this second part of the task, the analyst must overcome the *resistance* put up by the subject's conscience, the censor and guardian of consciousness, to admitting what has in the past been excluded. The theory is that once the resistance of the conscience is sufficiently lowered to allow admittance of the repressed impulse to consciousness, a process of *catharsis*, or purgation, sets in which dissipates the cathexis, or charge of psychic energy, attached to the impulse, and the latter itself will cease to exist. With the elimination of the cathected impulse through its admission to consciousness, all those devious forms of its circuitous expression, according to Freud's theory, should likewise disappear—the dream elements, the slips of tongue, the symptomatic actions, and, if the subject be a patient, the symptoms, associated with the particular repressed but now dissipated instinct-presentation.

Freud's further elaboration of the theory of repression involves his development of its separate elements. These elements include: instincts, infantile sexuality, The Unconscious, resistance, consciousness, sublimation, conscience, censorship, the principles of pleasure, pain and reality, and psychic energy. Here we will deal only with Freud's elaboration of his concept of *psychic energy* or cathexis. The remaining elements are dealt with in subsequent chapters.

As we have seen above, *psychic energy* is assigned a decisive role in the theory of repression. Of psychic energy, Freud said, "Without assuming the existence of a displaceable energy of this kind we can make no headway." We will find that psychic energy is the pillar of the theory of repression and the latter is the king-pin of psychoanalysis.

Freud's Concept of Psychic Energy

Freud conceived of psychic energy evidently by analogy with

the various forms of energy at work in the physical world—mechanical, thermal, electrical and chemical. Physiology views the human organism as a complicated energy system in which energy from food is used in such organic processes as circulation, respiration, digestion, nervous conduction and muscular and glandular activity generally. In addition to such physiological forms of mechanical, electrical and chemical energy, Freud assumed a *psychic energy* at work in the *psychological* processes of perceiving, remembering, thinking, etc. Psychic energy, according to Freud, performs psychological work just as mechanical energy, for example, performs mechanical work. Bodily energy, he maintains, is transformed into psychic energy and psychic energy may in turn be transformed into bodily energy. The force of the contraction of the stomach, for instance, is said to be transformed into the psychic energy of the hunger instinct. As a matter of fact, Freud regarded psychic energy as a whole to be predominantly *instinct energy*. Speaking of the mental apparatus, Freud says, "Almost all the energy with which this apparatus is filled arises from its innate instinctual impulses." The *amount* of psychic energy attached to any given instinctive impulse he regarded as being dependent on the force of the stimulus arising in the particular organ involved.

The specific psychic or instinct energy with which Freud was most concerned, and on which he did the most work, was that attached to the sexual instincts. He gave a special name to the psychic energy of the sexual instincts, *libido*. "In every way analogous to *hunger*," Freud says, "libido is the force by means of which the instinct, in this case the sexual instinct, as with hunger, the nutritional instinct, achieves expression."[6] Since, however, Freud conceived of psychic energy as displaceable, in the sense that the energy of one instinct could be detached and joined to the energy of another qualitatively different one, there was in fact no real reason for him to insist on libido as a special sexual psychic energy. Thus he says, "One can either drop the term 'libido' altogether, or use it as meaning the same as psychic energy in general."[7]

Freud is never very explicit about the concept of psychic energy. For example, he says, "We have reckoned as though there existed in the mind a displaceable energy, which is in itself neutral, but is able to join forces either with an erotic or with a destructive impulse, differing qualitatively as they do, and augment its total cathexis. Without assuming the existence of a displaceable energy of this kind we can make no headway. The only question is where it comes from, what it belongs to, and what it signifies." The energy *belongs to* an instinct which in turn is derived from an organic source. The significance of psychic energy is, according to Freud, that it furnishes all the energy employed in the mental apparatus, and can be made over from one instinctual impulse to another. He describes this work of psychic energy with regard to the sexual instincts: "In the sexual component-instincts, which are especially accessible to observation, it is possible to perceive the working of processes which are in the same category as what we are discussing; e.g., we see that some degree of communication exists between the component-instincts, that an instinct deriving from one particular erotogenic source can make over its intensity to reinforce another component-instinct originating in another source, that gratification of one instinct can take the place of gratification of another, and many more facts of the same nature."[8]

Psychic energy or libido, then, is a displaceable, neutral energy supplied by instincts which in turn receive this energy from the force of the stimuli emanating from the bodily organs. This is just about the sum total of Freud's development of the concept. He has, however, a great deal more to say about the *role* of psychic energy in the process of repression. We will be concerned with that role as we investigate, in the following chapters, Freud's psychology and psychopathology. At present we will limit our attention to what Freud calls the "economy of psycho-dynamics."

The cathexis or charge of psychic energy of an instinct is what gives that instinct its drive toward consciousness and toward motor expression. If the instinctive impulse is offensive to consciousness, in terms of conscientious norms, standards, values and beliefs, then consciousness must expend an equal amount of energy in repressing or pushing the charged or cathected instinctive impulse back out of consciousness. This counter-charge of psychic energy Freud calls an *anti-cathexis.* Cathexis comes from instincts, anti-cathexis comes from consciousness. The dynamic relations of the two comprise the *economy of psycho-dynamics*. For healthy functioning there must be a *dynamic equilibrium* of cathexes and anti-cathexes, of charges and counter-charges of psychic energy. An increase in intensity of the cathexis of an instinctive impulse, or of a repressed instinctive impulse, upsets the delicate balance of cathexis and anti-cathexis. Any increase in cathexis requires at least an equivalent increase in anti-cathexis.

"We may imagine," Freud says, "that what is repressed exercises a continuous straining in the direction of consciousness, so that the balance has to be kept by means of a steady counter-pressure. A constant expenditure of energy, therefore, is entailed in maintaining a repression, and economically its abrogation denotes a saving." A *fully successful* repression would be one in which the charge of psychic energy, the cathexis, was withdrawn or completely transferred. In such a case, the repressed impulse, shorn of its cathexis, could no longer exert pressure toward consciousness or behavior and would therefore require no anti-cathexis. In the case of *unsuccessful* repressions, the repressed instinctive impulse would retain its charge of psychic energy, and therefore a constant expenditure of psychic energy, a counter-charge or anti-cathexis, would be required to maintain the repression. In an unsuccessful repression, the retained cathexis would exert constant pressure against the anti-cathexis and would actually, from time to time, "outwit" it and gain entrance to consciousness by circuitous routes and under a multitude of disguises—dream images, slips of tongue, neurotic symptoms, etc.

The "economy" of the mental apparatus, the dynamic or unstable balance between instinct-cathexis and anti-cathexis, comprises Freud's dynamics of psychic life.

Freud's theory of repression constitutes an attempt to account for mental life in exclusively mental terms, without reference to the brain. The concept of *psychic energy* is his substitute for nervous energy, the chemical and electrical conduction of impulses in the central nervous system. The only evidence for such a mental energy is the requirement of the mental theory of repression. Thus Freud had to invent a mythical psychic energy in order to construct a purely mental view of mental processes. Pavlov, on the other hand, attempted to account for mental life in terms of higher cerebral activity in which the chemical and electrical energy of the central nervous system would be sufficient without assuming any hypothetical psychic energy. He employed the classical physiological reflex as the central concept in his science of higher nervous activity. In this manner he claimed to be able to account for mental phenomena without leaving the realm of established scientific procedure or concepts. The conditioned reflex constituted his great contribution toward an adequate physiological explanation of mental life.

We turn now to a confrontation of Freud's purely mental theory of repression and his concept of psychic energy by Pavlov's theory of the conditioned reflex and nervous energy.

Pavlov's Theory of the Conditioned Reflex

Pavlov employed the salivary fistula to investigate the physiology or mode of functioning of the highest part of the brain, the cerebral hemispheres.

In reporting his theory of the functioning of the cerebral hemispheres, Pavlov begins with the definition of the reflex as established by centuries of physiological research. *Reflex* is a scientific concept meaning that a certain agent of the external world, or of the internal organic system of the animal, produces a certain effect in one or another nervous receptor (eyes, nose, ears, skin, mucous membranes, etc.). This effect is then transformed into a nervous process, that is, into nervous excitation. The excitation is transmitted along certain nerve fibres to the central nervous system where previously established connections are made, or new ones opened. After this connective work has been done by the spinal chord or by certain parts of the brain, or by their combination, the excitation passes along other nerve fibres to a certain working organ (hand, foot, mouth, etc.) where it in turn is transformed into a special activity of the cells of this organ setting it into appropriate motion. Thus in a reflex the stimulating agent is the *cause* producing certain definite nervous and muscular or glandular *effects* in the animal organism, whether canine or human. This cause and effect relationship expresses discoverable lawful relations, just as do cause and effect relations throughout nature, living and non-living.

Pavlov's contribution begins with a distinction between inborn and acquired reflexes.

Signalling and the Conditioned Reflex

In the decorticated animal, only those stimuli acting in immediate proximity have any effect, and such stimuli are exceedingly limited and very general and undifferentiated in character. Minus the cortex, the animal can react solely to certain general features of the immediate environment. What is missing in such an animal is the entire *signalling* apparatus. The decorticated animal loses the power of reacting to signals and therefore suffers a profound *disequilibrium* with the environment. An entire half of its adaptation to surrounding conditions of life is wiped out. It retains only that part of adaptation which has become hereditary in the species in the form of inborn reflexes. Such reflexes are adaptations to the relatively permanent features of nature, those which remain essentially the same for hundreds and thousands of years.

The cortex, on the other hand, comprises the apparatus for continuous adaptation to changing environmental conditions from day to day. The cortical signalling system is itself constantly in a state of flux matching the state of flux of the less permanent features of the environment. Everyday life demands detailed and specialized correlations between the animal and the surrounding world. The signalling function of the hemispheres allows a large number of natural stimuli to act as temporary and alternate signals for the relatively small number of fundamental agents that determine the inborn reflexes. Only through this signalling activity of the hemispheres is a precise and delicate, yet forever changing adaptation of the organism to the environment attained.

The signalizing activity of the cerebral hemispheres displays the basic elements of nervous activity in general, namely, reflexes. The reflex mechanism underlies signalling, but it is a different kind of reflex from the inborn type. Signalling is a temporary and acquired reflex depending on conditions, time and place, while the reflex characteristic of the lower parts of the brain and central nervous system is permanent and inborn. For this reason Pavlov called the signal reflex *conditioned* and the inborn reflex *unconditioned*. The mode of functioning of the cerebral hemispheres is the conditioned reflex, according to Pavlov. He spent some thirty-five years in elaborating, experimentally, the facts and laws of the conditioned reflex; how it is formed, how it is refined and how it is extinguished. Here we can do no more than indicate a few of its general features.*

Synthesis: The Formation of Conditioned Connections

The primary condition for the formation of a temporary reflex is a single or, more often, repeated coincidence of the indifferent stimulus—which can be anything in the environment that is perceptible to the senses—with an inborn or unconditioned reflex. This fact, the cornerstone of Pavlov's theory, was established in literally thousands of experiments in which the most diverse phenomena from bells and flashing lights to skin irritations and odors, were formed into conditioned stimuli or signals standing for those objects, such as food and acid, which always set in motion the unconditioned reflex of salivation. These experiments demonstrated that anything whatever in the environment, limited only by the capacity of the sense organs, can act as a signal in the place of the usual unconditioned agent.

The formation of new conditioned reflexes, on the basis either of inborn reflexes or old conditioned ones, is the product of the nervous process called *excitation*. The mechanism of the connecting link is simple coincidence in time. Anything seen or heard or smelled several times immediately before the stimulation of one or another inborn reflex, for example feeding, becomes connected with the latter. In short the continued serial coincidence of two stimuli is sufficient to establish a new temporary reflex. The two stimuli can be a combination of either one conditioned and one unconditioned stimulus, or of two conditioned stimuli, one old and one new. Pavlov called

---

*For a detailed discussion of the conditioned reflex see *Pavlov and Freud*, Vol. I.

the process of establishing new conditioned connections *synthesis*.

Analysis: *The Refinement of Conditioned Connections*

Synthesis, however, is only a beginning in the process of adaptation or dynamic equilibrium between the animal organism and the environment. New conditioned connections are, at the outset crude. A conditioned connection, for example, between a given sound and food, spreads to include almost any sound. A second process, in addition to synthesis, is required if the adaptation or equilibrium is to be truly effective. *Analysis* of the new temporary reflex connection is the next step. Not just *any* sound will serve as an effective warning indicating danger to an animal. The sound must be pinpointed to that particular sound made by such and such an enemy.

This process of analytical refinement of conditioned reflexes is the task of the other basic nervous component, *inhibition*. Inhibition and excitation, according to Pavlov, constitute the two essential aspects of *higher* nervous activity, just as they do of *lower* nervous functioning.

Inhibition, in its role as analyser, is primarily *adaptive* in function. In general it is the construction of blockages to excitation through lack of reinforcement of conditioned stimuli. In nature, from birth, this process takes place. The animal is constantly stimulated by various sounds, but in the course of experience it reacts only to those which have proven effective in, for example, procuring food; avoiding danger or finding a mate. But technically, the animal has in the process of growing up, built inhibitions to those conditioned stimuli which have not been reenforced by satisfying inborn reflexes, and on the other hand has established strongly entrenched conditioned reflexes to those stimuli which have been so reenforced. Thus analysis through inhibition is just as vital an activity of the higher nervous activity of the cerebral hemispheres in animals as is synthesis through excitation. The one without the other would lead to destructive disequilibrium between the organism and the environment.

The process of analysis is in fact refinement of adaptive behavior. In the animal it *appears* as intelligence, perception, even thought and judgment. It is the major reason why people have been able to attribute *human* mental characteristics to animals. It does *appear* as though the animal was exhibiting a high degree of conscious activity and ability. The fact, according to Pavlov, is that the delicate apparatus of animal higher nervous activity, the work of the cerebral hemispheres, can account for the most complex animal behavior without assuming possession of a single mental attribute of man.

Extinction: Forgetting and Remembering in Animals

Another closely related form of adaptive inhibition is the process of *extinction* of conditioned reflexes. Just as important as the formation of new conditioned connections is their elimination when they are no longer required by the animal. In other words, "forgetting" is as important as "learning" in the first place, or as "remembering." For example, a sound which had become a signal or conditioned stimulus standing for danger, could itself become a danger, or at least a liability, if it continued beyond the time when it was an effective signal.

Pavlov found that conditioned reflexes are inhibited, wither away and cease to operate whenever they are not reinforced periodically by the unconditioned reflex for which they stand as sign. Actually such extinction of conditioned connections takes place continuously in nature. Every change in environment, moving from one locale to another, if it is a relatively permanent change, requires extinction of some of the old signals and formation of new ones.

Conditioned reflexes can be, and are forever being, extinguished as well as formed. They can likewise be reformed or "remembered" by the simple process of reenforcing them just once with the related unconditioned reflex. Thus if a given sound, which had been a conditioned stimulus for feeding, is extinguished as such, it can later be recalled by once again accompanying the sound by actual feeding.

The three processes of formation, extinction and re-formation of conditioned reflexes roughly correspond to what is known in human beings as "learning," "forgetting" and "remembering."

In this brief summary of Pavlov's investigation of the cerebral hemispheres, we have omitted, among other things, his work on the specifically human phenomena. We have been concerned only with the most elementary components expressing the general functioning of higher nervous activity, those which Pavlov held to be common to man and and animals alike.

Confrontation of the Two Theories

In this confrontation of Freud's theory of repression by Pavlov's theory of the conditioned reflex, at least two striking contrasts appear in bold relief.

Freud starts with two observations and proceeds to build a giant superstructure of assumptions to account for them. To explain the forgetting of painful events and the resistance to their recall to consciousness, he assumes, in addition to sexual and death instincts, *cathexis* or *psychic energy, censorship* or *anti-cathexis, retention of cathexis* after repression, and finally *circuitous routes* and *disguises* by means of which repressed impulses gain entrance to consciousness.*

Pavlov, on the other hand, developed his theory of acquired or ontogenetic higher activity, the conditioned reflex, entirely as generalizations from experimentally derived facts. These generalizations were then tested and revised in the course of innumerable further experiments, leading eventually to verified, and verifiable, laws and theoretical conclusions. Further, he based his experimental work with the conditioned reflex on the already established scientific theory of the *reflex* character of nervous activity generally. He simply applied the verified concept of the reflex to higher nervous activity.

Likewise, Pavlov viewed the function of both the innate and

*The circular reasoning involved in Freud's theory of repression is indicated by the fact that the analyst in the first place "discovers" the unconscious, forgotten, *repressed* impulses by means of interpretation of dream images, slips of tongue, symptomatic actions and unconscious associations. In the second place, the theory, after numerous other assumptions, assumes that these very same dream images, slips, actions and associations are circuitous routes or disguises by means of which repressed impulses gain entrance to conciousness. Thus, the theory ends up with its tail in its mouth. For the final step, the circuitous routes and disguises, must already be assumed in the first step, the discovery of forgotten material—since the analyst discovers the forgotten material only by means of interpreting dreams, slips, actions, etc., as circuitous routes and disguises of repressed impulses.

acquired higher nervous activity as concerned with *adaptation.* Adaptation of organism to environment had already become an established fact through the work of biologists, in the first place, Darwin. Freud, however, viewed the work of both innate and acquired higher mental activity as concerned not primarily with adaptation but with an intramural struggle between instincts and consciousness. In this, a further assumption, Freud was in sharp opposition to the established facts and laws of other sciences, particularly biology.

In general, a comparison of the theories of repression and the conditioned reflex shows Freud relying heavily on speculatively derived assumptions and Pavlov just as heavily relying on experimentally derived facts.

Freud, himself, always made a fully conscious and explicit distinction between his *observations* and his *assumptions.* The latter were made to account for the former—but he consistently maintained that it was the lack of scientific knowledge in other fields, notably physiology and biology, which forced the psychologist to make speculative assumptions.

It is, of course, true that the speculative assumptions in Freud's theory of repression can *theoretically,* as a logical system, account for the observed facts of forgetting and resistance. But if a strictly scientific theory, experimentally derived, can also account for them as well as other observations, then the history of all the sciences bears testimony to the inevitable verdict in favor of the latter as the true theory.

Whether Pavlov's theory of higher nervous activity with its unconditioned and conditioned reflexes fills this description, it is too early in the present volume to say definitively. A final verdict must again be postponed until, in the following chapters, we have seen Pavlov's theories at work in explaining human phenomena. It might be pointed out here, however, that in the nervous processes of inhibition and excitation there exist the elements for explaining "forgetting" and "recalling" at least in animals. The former is the process of extinguishing a conditioned reflex through omitting to reenforce it, and the latter is the process of re-forming it by once again reenforcing it.

Here also a warning is in order. The science of higher nervous activity cannot as yet furnish a basis to account for *all,* or even a large part, of psychic phenomena. Experimental science progresses slowly from fact to fact—relatively slowly, that is, to the leaps and bounds of speculation.

In the over-all confrontation of Freud's theory of the conditioned reflex, there can at this stage be no one to one comparison. The central point is that while Freud created a speculative theory which immediately could give an account of all mental phenomena, Pavlov laid a solid foundation which through patient experimental work holds the promise of eventual solution of the age-old riddle of man's mind. The crucial problem posed by this confrontation is whether further progress in psychology and psychiatry is to be made along the lines suggested by Freud or those indicated by Pavlov. Do psychic energy and repression furnish the basis for a scientific understanding of mental life, or do nervous energy and reflex activity furnish this basis?

There are a few points of almost one to one comparison of Freud and Pavlov which can help in finding the answer. In the following chapters the two approaches will meet head-on in opposite explanations of such "mental" phenomona as: instincts, sleep, dreams, hypnosis, hypnotic suggestion, and neuroses.

The first area of one to one comparison is instinctive or inborn activity. Here there is a confrontation of Freud's theory of instincts by Pavlov's theory of the unconditioned reflex.

Chapter IV

INSTINCTS AND UNCONDITIONED REFLEXES

ONE OF THE most intriguing problems in man's view of himself is the nature, role and extent of inborn reactions, known traditionally as "instincts." Down the centuries philosophers, scientists and poets have wrestled with the great issue of whether man is controlled by innate instincts or by acquired habits learned in the course of actual living. Intellectual history has tended to swing from one extreme position to the other: either instincts or habits govern mankind. In the twentieth century, Freud has come to personify the exclusive stress on instincts while J. B. Watson and the Behaviorists have represented the other extreme, exclusive stress on environment, habit and learning. When either of these extreme positions is confronted by the other, there is more often than not merely fruitless assertion and counter-assertion in an unending controversy.

When, however, the instinct theory is confronted by another theory of the nature, role and extent of innate activity, then it is possible to come to some kind of conclusion as to their relative merits. Pavlov does not deny innate activity as the Behaviorists have done. On the contrary, he shows experimentally that there can be no learning at all without inborn reactions. The latter form the ultimate basis for all acquired behavior. Thus the confrontation of Freud's theory of instincts by Pavlov's theory of innate or unconditioned reflexes is on a quite different level than, for example, a confrontation of Freud by Watson. The conflict between Freud and Pavlov on this question is not *whether* there is innate activity, but rather revolves around the problem of its nature. Thus a comparison of the two positions should help in settling the over-all issue as to whether Pavlov or Freud holds greater promise in man's attempt to understand himself.

We begin with Freud's theory of instincts.

FREUD'S THEORY OF INSTINCTS

"The theory of instincts," Freud writes, "is, as it were, our mythology." And he adds, "The instincts are mythical beings, superb in their indefiniteness. In our work we cannot for a moment overlook them, and yet we are never certain that we are seeing them clearly."[1] Elsewhere he speaks of "the organism's instincts" as "at once the most important and the most obscure element of psychological research."[2]

He complained that neither biology nor physiology could supply psychology with a scientific theory of instincts, and therefore there was no alternative but to make assumptions about them. "No knowledge," Freud wrote, "would have been more valuable as a foundation for true psychological knowledge than an approximate grasp of the common characteristics and possible distinctive features of the instincts. But in no region of psychology were we groping more in the dark. Everyone assumed the existence of as many instincts or 'basic instincts' as he chose, and juggled with them like the ancient Greek natural philosophers with their four elements—earth, air, fire and water. Psychoanalysis . . . could not escape making *some* assumptions about the instincts."[3]

Freud calls *instinct* "a conventional but still rather obscure basal concept which is nevertheless indispensable to us in psychology." He considers instinct from the "biological" point of view "as a borderland concept between the mental and the physical."[4] It is the mental representative of the stimuli coming from within the organism. An instinct is "physical" with regard to the stimulus which comes from one or another internal organ of the body; and it is at the same time "mental" with regard to a certain quality of feeling recognized as instinctual excitement. For example, the sex instinct's mental representative appears in the form of a certain quality of feeling, recognized as sexual excitement, emanating from the genital zone. Thus an instinct, according to Freud, is a mental reflection of the needs of various bodily organs.

Since in any psychology the question of inborn activity is of extreme importance, Freud had to take up some position on it. His position, like that of any psychologist so long as verified facts and laws are non-existent, was of necessity *speculative*. His theory of instincts is the product of two considerations: first, the requirements of his own psychological system as a whole; and second, concern not to contravene such few facts as were currently known on the basis of other sciences. His position on the *nature* of instincts was not, in point of fact, much different from that of other contemporary psychologists, including, for example, William James. In short, lacking a physiology of the higher parts of the nervous system, psychologists, Freud among them, could do no more than make the best of a bad situation with regard to the nature of instincts.

Where he differs fundamentally from other psychologists on the question, is his *choice* and *classification* of instincts. When there is no verified knowledge, there is ample room for arbitrary choice. "Now what instincts and how many should be postulated?" Freud asks, and he immediately remarks, "There is obviously a great opportunity here for arbitrary choice." Since there was currently no systematic body of scientifically established facts about instincts, no real objections could be raised against anyone's choice. "No objection can be made," Freud says, "to anyone's employing the concept of an instinct of play or of destruction, or that of a social instinct, when the subject demands it and the limitations of psychological analysis allow of it." But he suggests that perhaps, underlying all the profuse array of postulated instincts, there may be a limited number of "primal instincts which can not be resolved further."

Before presenting his own choice of "primal instincts," Freud once more decries the lack of knowledge of instincts. If only other sciences such as physiology and biology had successfully investigated the problem, it would not be necessary for psychology to make arbitrary assumptions. "I am altogether doubtful," Freud says, "whether work upon psychological material will afford any decisive indication for the distinction and classification of instincts. Rather it would seem necessary to apply to this material certain definite assumptions in order to work upon it, and we could wish that these assumptions might be taken from some other branch of knowledge and transferred to psychology." [5]

Since such a transference was precluded, Freud had to make his own assumptions—on the basis of the requirements of his particular subject, while as far as possible avoiding conflict with any currently known scientific facts. "We suppose," he says, "that there are two fundamentally different kinds of instincts, the sexual instincts (Eros, if you prefer that name) and the aggressive instincts, whose aim is destruction." Their proper psychoanalytic *names* are the *erotic instincts* and the *death instincts*. "And now," Freud says, "the instincts in which we believe separate themselves into two groups: the erotic instincts, which are always trying to collect living substance together into ever larger unities, and the death instincts, which act against that tendency, and try to bring living matter back into an inorganic condition." [6]

The erotic or sexual instincts are, according to Freud, numerous and emanate from several organic sources. The aim of each is to attain "organ pleasure." Of the several organic sources, or erotogenic zones, three play a decisive role, the oral zone, the anal zone and the genital zone. We will see later (Chapters VI and VII) the essential significance of these zones as *phases* in Freud's theory of character development and as fixations and repressions in his theory of the psycho-neuroses.

The death instincts, including "a special instinct of aggression and destruction in man," [7] have as their aim the dissolution of life and the reinstatement of the inorganic state. Satisfaction of the death instinct lies in both self-destruction and the destruction of others. Freud was never able to say wherein lay the bodily source of these instincts. His main evidence for them was, on the one hand, war and violence generally, and on the other, the perversion phenomena of masochism and sadism.

Of this conversion to belief in the death instinct, Freud wrote, "On the basis of speculations concerning the origin of life and of biological parallels, I drew the conclusion that, beside the instinct preserving the organic substance and binding it into ever-larger units, there must exist another in antithesis to this, which would seek to dissolve these units and reinstate their antecedent inorganic state; that is to say, a death instinct as well as Eros; the phenomena of life would then be explicable from the interplay of the two and their counteracting effects on each other. It was not easy however to demonstrate the working of this hypothetical death instinct. The manifestations of Eros were conspicuous and audible enough; one might assume that the death instinct worked silently within the organism towards its disintegration, but that, of course, was no proof. . . . The assumpion of the existence of a death instinct or a destruction instinct has aroused opposition even in analytical circles. . . . The conceptions I have summarized here I first put forward only tentatively, but in the course of time they have won such a hold over me that I can no longer think in any other way."

In the form of the death instinct, Freud maintains that "the tendency to aggression is an innate, independent, instinctual disposition in man," and he speaks of "the natural instinct of aggressiveness in man, the hostility of each one against all, and of all against each one." He adds that "This instinct of aggression is the derivative and main representative of the death instinct we have found alongside of Eros, sharing his rule over the earth." [8]

Noting the almost universal opposition to his concept of the death instinct, Freud recognizes that it shocks and outrages the popular notion that man is by nature good, that if he occasionally resorts to violence, aggression and war, these are the result of "the ill-adapted social system which he has so far made for himself." "Unfortunately," Freud says, "the testimony of history and our own experience do not bear this out, but rather confirm the judgment that the belief in the 'goodness' of man's nature is one of those illusions from which mankind expects some kind of beautifying or amelioration of their lot, but which in reality bring only disaster." [9]

Not only the death instinct with its aggressive and destructive tendencies, but also the sexual instinct with its oral and anal phases, fixations and repressions, were rudely shocking and outrageous to people everywhere and in all walks of life. Freud, however, maintained that this shock and outrage merely underscored his theory of repression. When the unconscious instincts, those based on aggression and sexual perversion, reached consciousness in one form or another, through dreams and unwanted impulses, thoughts and emotions, the conscience was so shocked and outraged that it forthwith repressed them back into the unconscious. This, in fact, is the essence of repression and forms a basis of psychoanalytical theory.

We will find that the death and sexual instincts, together with the various *vicissitudes* or changes which they undergo, comprise the essential subject-matter of both Freud's psychology and his psychopathology. Chief among these vicissitudes is *repression*. Others are, according to Freud, *reversal into its opposite, turning round upon the subject, fixation, regression and sublimation*. We will see all these, in later chapters, at work in his theory of character formation and his theory of the psychoneuroses.

Freud's theory of instincts is not only, as he once said, his "mythology." It is more importantly a cornerstone of his theory of repression which in turn is the heart and center of psychoanalysis.

We turn now to a brief account of Pavlov's theory of unconditioned reflexes.

Pavlov's Theory of the Unconditioned Reflex

Prior to Pavlov's work on the reflex activity of the cerebral hemispheres, physiological investigation had been exclusively concerned with the *inborn*, constant reflexes. For a long time only those innate reflexes related to the functioning of separate organs were the subject of study. But there are other, more complex inborn reactions, those that have traditionally been called *instincts*. These instinctive reactions also take place in the nervous system, and are governed by laws expressing cause and effect relationships strictly determined by external and internal conditions. Instincts are the reactions of different animals in relation to the functioning of the organism as a whole, manifested in general behavior, such as defensive, feeding, mating and migrating instincts.

Herbert Spencer, the British philosopher, was among the first to suggest that instincts are expressions of reflex activity. Following this suggestion, zoologists, physiologists and comparative psychologists produced numerous facts in support of this theory. At the time Pavlov developed his theory, however, full agreement of the experts on this subject had not yet been reached. Hence in his report of his theory in 1923, Pavlov marshalled the current arguments in support of the position that "there is not a single essential feature distinguishing reflexes from instincts."[10] Here is a summary of these arguments.

First of all there are numerous, imperceptible stages of transition from the usual reflexes to instincts. Take, for example, a newly hatched chick; it reacts by pecking movements to any stimulus in the field of its vision, be it a tiny object or a stain on the surface on which it is walking. In what way does it differ, say, from inclining the head and closing the lids when something flashes near the eye? While traditionally the latter is called a defensive reflex, and the first an alimentary instinct, there is in truth no difference between the two. The pecking of the chick is actually nothing but the reflex of inclining the head and moving the beak when set in motion by external agents, namely tiny objects and stains.

Second, it has been noted that instincts are more complex than reflexes. But there are highly complex reflexes which no one designates as instincts, for example vomiting. The latter is an extremely complex action, one that involves extraordinary coordination of a large number of muscles usually employed in other functions of the organism and spread over a large area. It also involves secretion of various glands which normally participate in quite different activities.

Third, the fact that instincts involve a long chain of successive actions, while reflexes are, so to speak, one-storeyed, has been regarded as a point of distinction between them. By way of example, let us take the building of a nest, or of animal dwellings in general. Here, of course, we have a long chain of actions; the animal must search for the material, bring it to the site, put it together and secure it. To regard this as reflex activity it is necessary that there be a mechanism in which the termination of one reflex is the stimulus for the initiation of the next, that the end of one reflex excites a succeeding one, a kind of *chain of reflexes*. Such a mechanism is quite familiar in reflex activity. There are many reflexes that are interlocked. For example, when a certain nerve is stimulated there takes place a rise in blood pressure. The end of this first reflex is the stimulus which sets in motion a second reflex moderating the effect of the first. R. Magnus established the chain-reflex underlying the well-known fact that a cat, no matter how thrown, will always land on its feet. A certain change in the ear sets in motion a certain reflex contraction of the muscles in the neck which restores the cat's head to a normal position in relation to the horizon. The end of this first reflex sets in motion a fresh reflex on certain muscles of the body and legs which restores the animal's proper standing posture. Thus a chain of successive actions forms no line of demarcation between reflexes and instincts.

Fourth, still another difference between reflexes and instincts has been assumed, namely, that instincts often depend on the internal state or condition of the organism. For example, a bird builds its nest only in the mating season, or when an animal is sated it is no longer attracted by food. But this is not a property of instincts alone. The intensity of any reflex, as well as its presence or absence, directly depends on the state of excitability of the reflex centers which in turn depend on the chemical and physical properties of the blood and on the interaction of different reflexes.

Finally, importance has sometimes been attached to the fact that reflexes are related to the activity of separate organs, whereas instincts involve the activity of the whole skeletomuscular system. The works of Magnus and de Kleyn, however, have conclusively demonstrated that such all-inclusive skeletomuscular activity as bodily balance, standing and walking is the product of reflexes.

From these arguments Pavlov draws his conclusion: "Thus reflexes and instincts alike are natural reactions of the organism to certain stimulating agents, and consequently there is no need to designate them by different terms. The term *reflex* is preferable, since a strictly scientific sense has been imparted to it from the very outset." The so-called instincts are, according to Pavlov, *inborn chains of reflexes*. The inborn chain-reflexes together with the innate single reflexes "constitute," he says, the foundation of the nervous activity in men and animals." [11]

It might at first appear that Pavlov is making a semantical

distinction between the terms "instinct" and "reflex." The latter he says is preferable because it has had a scientific meaning from the beginning. The preference here is however pregnant with objective reference. The chains of reflexes, of which Pavlov speaks, are extensions of the meaning of simple reflexes. As such they are reactions to the external world as it impinges on the animal or human organism. Inborn chains of reflexes, what Pavlov calls unconditioned reflexes, are those adaptive reactions to the more permanent features of the environment which through hundreds of thousands of years have become hereditary. Those hereditary chain reflexes embody the higher animal's, including man's, adaptation, at a species level, to the world around them.

Without such inborn, unconditioned reflexes there would be no basis on which individual learning could take place. This individual learning is concerned with the adaptation of the individual to the less permanent, more temporary and more changing features of the circumambient world. The conditioned reflex is, according to Pavlov, the nervous mechanism of the learning process. This process depends on temporary sensory and verbal signals being reenforced by unconditioned reflexes. If there were no such inborn reactions, there could be no reenforcement, and if there were no reenforcement there could be no acquiring of conditioned reflexes, in short no learning. For example, if there were no pain or defensive unconditioned reflexes, an animal or a child could not learn to avoid hot or sharp objects. This is what Pavlov means when he says that unconditioned reflexes form the basis for the entire higher nervous activity of animals and men.

While the innate unconditioned reflexes are highly important and indispensible, they are at the same time sharply limited in their functioning. They are crude and blind and therefore require learning or conditioned reflex activity to make the subtle distinctions and refinements necessary for effective animal or human functioning in the environmental situation. There are, according to Pavlov, relatively few higher nervous unconditioned reflexes, and even these are only a foundation on which the psychic activity of the animal or man must be acquired during a life-time.

The great advantage of Pavlov's conception of unconditioned reflexes, as opposed to instincts, is that it guides experimental work in the discovery of their precise number, nature and role. It allows no room for speculation, but rather places the emphasis on scientific determination of innate higher nervous activity. Without such determination anyone is free to assume such instincts as might be dictated by individual predilection, theoretical bias or systemic requirement. Freud by his own admission belongs to this latter category.

When we compare the two approaches, two main conclusions force themselves upon us.

We note on the one hand that Freud's conception of the inborn or phylogenetic element in higher activity follows the traditional and popular notion of quasi-mental instincts, while, on the other, Pavlov, building on the already established knowledge of reflex activity, develops a theory in which chains of reflexes account for innate higher activity. Pavlov's theory of *unconditioned* reflexes brought the phenomena traditionally called "instincts" out of the realm of speculation and placed them in the laboratory where their nature and classification could be experimentally established.

Freud, however, retained the vague concept of instincts, and tailored their nature and classification to meet the requirements of his system. His classification of the instincts into sexual (oral, anal and genital) and death (aggressive and destructive) is closer to the speculations of certain philosophers—Nietzsche, Schopenhauer, William James—than to scientifically determined hypotheses. Freud, himself, was aware of this, and, as we have seen, bemoaned the current lack of knowledge on the subject. Thus with regard to the inborn higher activity Freud resorted to more or less arbitrary *assumptions,* while Pavlov relied on carefully controlled *experimentation.*

With regard to this first area of one to one comparison, therefore, we must conclude that Pavlov furnishes the more scientific basis for the eventual understanding of man's innate, so-called instinctive, higher (psychic) activity.

The next point of comparison concerns the three systems of psychic activity worked out respectively by Freud and Pavlov.

Chapter V

THE UNCONSCIOUS AND THE SCIENCE OF HIGHER NERVOUS ACTIVITY

Pavlov and Freud, in the course of their respective work, differentiated three separate but interacting functional systems of higher activity in human beings. Freud conceived of human higher activity as purely mental, though undoubtedly resting on an anatomical and physiological base, which would some day be discovered. Pavlov conceived of the basis of human higher activity in terms of the cerebral hemispheres and their functioning, the understanding of which would some day make possible a full elucidation of man's psychic life.

On the one hand, Freud took the position that psychology and psycho-pathology could not wait until a physiology of the cerebral hemispheres was developed, but had in the meantime to proceed as though mental life were completely independent of the brain.

On the other hand, Pavlov took the position that psychology and psychiatry could not develop much further as *sciences* until the physiology of higher nervous activity had laid a firm foundation on which they could be built.

We will be in a better position to weigh these opposite contentions after we have compared the three systems of higher activity presented respectively by Freud and by Pavlov.

Freud's Three Systems of Mental Activity

In his metapsychology, Freud attempts to view the *mental apparatus* as a whole and to ascertain its component systems. He speaks of "our attempt to make intelligible the complication of the psychic performance by dissecting it and referring the individual performances to the individual components of the apparatus." Since such a thing has never been done before, he proceeds by means of conjecture. "So far as I am aware," he continues, "no attempt has yet been made to divide the construction of the psychic instrument by means of such dissection. I see no harm in such an attempt; I think that we should give free rein to our conjectures, provided we keep our heads and do not mistake the scaffolding for the building." He indicates what kind of conjectured hypotheses he will employ. "Since for the first approach to any unknown subject we need the help only of auxiliary ideas, we shall prefer the crudest and most tangible hypotheses to all others."[1]

Freud was aware of the limitations of his venture. "Research has afforded," he says, "irrefutable proof that mental activity is bound up with the function of the brain as with that of no other organ. The discovery of the unequal importance of the different parts of the brain and their individual relations to particular parts of the body and to intellectual activities takes us a step further—we do not know how big a step. But every attempt to deduce from these facts a localization of mental processes, every endeavor to think of ideas as stored up in nerve-cells and of excitation as passing along nerve-fibres, has completely miscarried. The same fate would await any doctrine which attempted to recognize, let us say, the anatomical position of . . . conscious mental activity in the cortex and to localize the unconscious processes in the sub-cortical parts of the brain. Here there is an hiatus which at present cannot be filled, nor is it one of the tasks of psychology to fill it. Our mental topography has for the present nothing to do with anatomy; it is concerned not with anatomical locations, but with regions in the mental apparatus, irrespective of their possible situation in the body. In this respect, then, our work is untrammelled and may proceed according to its own requirements."

His conclusion is, "We shall ignore the fact that the psychic apparatus concerned is known to us also as an anatomical preparation, and we shall carefully avoid the temptation to determine the psychic locality in any anatomical sense. We shall remain on psychological ground. . . ."[2] As we know, and as

Freud well knew, this decision was by no means a matter of free choice, but was strictly determined by the contemporary gap in cerebral knowledge. Lacking such knowledge, any attempt to *divine* the nature of the mental apparatus had of necessity to be pure metapsychology, namely, psychological speculation, the psychological counterpart of *metaphysics*. The latter has always been, historically, in any field a *substitute* for scientific knowledge.

In the course of his life, Freud developed two general theories of the mental apparatus. The first was maintained from the turn of the century to about 1920,[3] and is dealt with in the present chapter. The second, essentially a refinement of the first, held sway from 1921 until his death in 1939,[4] and is dealt with in the following chapter.

The Conscious, The Preconscious and the Unconscious Systems of the Mental Apparatus.

In his first general metapsychological theory, Freud conjectured that the mental apparatus is composed of three systems: The conscious (Cs) the pre-conscious (Pcs) and The Unconscious (Ucs). To get an idea of what these three topographical systems—their *dynamics* and their *economics*—mean to Freud, we will first examine each separately and then see how he puts them into operation as a unified, functioning, mental apparatus. We begin, as Freud himself does, with The Unconscious.

1. *The Unconscious* (Ucs). The Unconscious is assumed by Freud to be a *locality* in the mental apparatus. It is composed of processes: First, instinct-presentations arising from stimuli originating in bodily organs, together with repressed impulses, wishes and ideas based on instincts; second, all those ideas, impulses and wishes which are *temporarily* unconscious but which can relatively easily become conscious. The latter type of unconscious processes, those which are readily admitted to consciousness, are not in the strictest sense part of The Unconscious. They comprise the subconscious or pre-conscious system, the Pcs.

The heart of The Unconscious, according to Freud, consists of instinct-presentations, or in other words, wish-impulses expressing instinctive drives. Instinctive wish-impulses are highly charged with psychic energy, that is, they are strongly cathected, and therefore ceaselessly and restlessly strive for admission to consciousness and thence for motor discharge. The Unconscious is thus conceived as a seething, writhing mass of instinctive activity, directed toward two things only—conscious recognition and active satisfaction.

The Ucs is unmoral, illogical, timeless and ultimately irresistible and irrepressible. It is the agency of the impersonal, elemental forces of creation and destruction, sex and aggression, life and death. The only regulation to which it will peaceably submit is the pleasure principle. Its only law is the seeking of pleasure through instinct gratification and the avoidance of the pain of instinct denial. Thus the Ucs is related just as little to reality as to time. Only the timeless psychic reality of pleasure is relevant to its functioning.

The principle of contradiction does not apply to The Unconscious. Contradictory instinctive wish-impulses exist side by side and even cooperatively lend one another their charges of psychic energy. The final arbiter of the fate of wish-impulses rests solely on the force of the psychic energy, the cathexis, which they can command.

All the repressed and discarded phases through which an instinct passes in the development from child to adult exist side by side in the Ucs, retaining their charges of psychic energy and therefore continuing throughout life to press for conscious recognition and motor expression. For Freud this means that the wish-impulses of the oral, anal and genital infantile phases of the sex instinct, for example, continue to exist in the adult as repressed and cathected processes in The Unconscious. He calls this side by side coexistence of temporal phases of instincts the *principle of ambivalence*. We will see in the following chapters that this principle plays an important part in his theories of character formation and the etiology of neuroses.

"Unconscious processes," Freud says, "can only be observed by us under the conditions of dreaming and of neurosis." [5] And even under these conditions, the Ucs becomes observable only with the aid of the psychoanalytical technique of dream interpretation with its symbol-reading, free association and transference phenomena. As evidence in support of his assumption of

The Unconscious he cites such phenomena as "association by Unconscious links."[6] the so-called "parapraxes" (slips of tongue and pen, forgetting of names, and the like) and "symptomatic actions";[7] "hypnotic suggestion";[8] "dreams";[9] and "neuroses."[10] All of these phenomena are effects which must have causes. There can be no question that they are effects, and common ones at that, but what are their causes? Freud maintains, correctly, that *consciousness cannot account for such phenomenal effects.* He goes on, however, to assume that unconscious, instinctive ideas, impulses and wishes, prohibited from direct entry into consciousness and from motor discharge, account for them in the form of disguised and circuitous means of entry and discharge. *Thus, for Freud, the cause of dreams, neuroses, and their like, is to be found primarily in the irresistible instinct activity of the unconscious system of the mental apparatus.*

We see, therefore, that the evidence Freud cites in support of The Unconscious, actually rests on the assumption that unconscious and instinctive mental activities cause dreams. He then cites the latter in evidence for the very processes of the mental Ucs which he has already assumed. His argument is circular. His theory of dreams involves Unconscious instinctive ideas, and yet he employs his theory of dreams and of neurosis as evidence for the very existence of The Unconscious comprised of instinct-ideas.

2. *The pre-conscious* (Pcs). We will recall that the pre-conscious system, in Freud's view, is composed of all those ideas, wishes and impulses which, while temporarily unconscious, can nevertheless become conscious with relative ease. The primary function of the Pcs is to set up and administer the censorship which stands guard, according to Freud, between The Unconscious and pre-conscious. Its task is to keep out of the Pcs all the unwanted, painful, disgusting, shocking, unmoral, illogical, contradictory instinctive wish-impulses from The Unconscious, together with their super-charged cathexes of psychic energy. The task of censorship, assigned to the Pcs, is a vital one for the theory of repression.

For the pre-conscious to fulfill its primary role as censor, it must be the repository of all memories coming originally from sense perception of the external world. It must include, as Freud holds, verbal associations which store up the social, moral, ethical, and religious standards, norms and values which comprise what is called the human *conscience.*

Conscience comprises the core of the Pcs censorship. But there is an additional element in the make-up of the censoring agency. The pre-conscious establishes the *reality principle* in opposition to the pleasure principle that rules over the Unconscious. The reality principle tests ideas, wishes, impulses and their like according to their truth or falsity, namely whether or not they correspond to external reality. The reality principle with its concern for truth is an ingredient in the Pcs censorship because it demands the subordination of instinct gratification to such social necessities as holding a job, making a living, conforming to social customs, carrying on engineering, scientific and cultural pursuits. All these require the repression of immediate instinctive "organ pleasure" in favor of the deferred and sublimated pleasures which, as by-products rather than as ends in themselves, accompany the social pursuits.

The moral conscience and social consciousness combine in the pre-conscious to constitute an ideal for the self, an "ego-ideal," which acts as the censor to keep intrusive instinct-impulses within the seething confines of The Unconscious. The Ucs is a kind of detention camp for the instincts, with the ego-ideal acting as ever vigilant guard. Following this analogy, the prisoners within the camp, full of energy and scheming cunning, constantly make direct assaults on the guard, and when these fail, employ the most devious methods and disguises to slip by the guard. The more pressure the guard employs in foiling these attempts, the more insistent become the forays.

Some of the disguises work and some instinctive impulses succeed in slipping through into the pre-conscious. Here they retain their charges of psychic energy and set up an insistent clamor to enter consciousness. The theory of repression then demands, according to Freud, that there be an additional censorship, one between the Pcs and conscious systems. The second censor brings us to the final and highest system in Freud's view of the mental apparatus.

3. *The conscious (Cs).* Freud has relatively little to say about consciousness proper. This is, of course, due to his systematic

stress on the completely predominant role of unconscious mental activity in opposition to the generally held opinion of mankind that consciousness is our most prized and valuable possession, one of the attributes which separate us from the rest of the animal kingdom. "In proportion as we try to win our way to a metapsychological view of mental life," Freud says, "we must learn to emancipate ourselves from our sense of the importance of that symptom which consists in 'being conscious.'"[11] He berates traditional psychology for its identification of the mental with the conscious.

Together with traditional psychology, Freud identifies consciousness with immediate awareness, either as current sense experience or as current feelings of pleasure and pain or as conceptions currently before the mind. In short, *he identifies consciousness with attention and assigns all other mental phenomena to the Ucs and Pcs systems.* "Now let us call 'conscious,'" he says, "the conception which is present to our consciousness and of which we are aware, and let this be the only meaning of the term 'conscious.'" And he adds, "As for latent conceptions, if we have any reason to suppose that they exist in the mind—as we had in the case of memory—let them be denoted by the term 'Unconscious' (Pcs)."[12]

With regard to consciousness, Freud registers the same complaint that he makes with regard to all other mental phenomena, namely the paucity of knowledge of them from other sources such as anatomy and physiology. "It must be borne in mind," he says, "that little enough is known from other sources of the origin of consciousness." And he is thereby impelled explicitly to warn the reader that "What follows is speculation, often farfetched speculation, which the reader will consider or dismiss according to his individual predilection."

"Psychoanalytic speculation" reduces consciousness to the limited function of registering internal and external perceptions. Thus like the household god, Janus, the system Cs faces two ways, outside and inside. It faces the outside world through excitations coming from the sense organs; and it faces the internal depths of the *Unconscious* systems (Pcs and Ucs) of the mental apparatus. On the basis of this double aspect, Freud assigns consciousness "a position in space." "It must lie," he says, on the borderline between outside and inside; it must be turned towards the external world and must envelop the other psychical systems." Freud rationalizes this *theory of localization of mental functions,* with its topographical representation, by an analogy with cerebral anatomy. "It will be seen," he says, "that there is nothing daringly new in these assumptions; we have merely adopted the views on localization held by cerebral anatomy, which locates the 'seat' of consciousness in the cerebral cortex—the outermost, enveloping layer of the central organ."

Freud, however, does not only employ the analogy with cerebral anatomy to support his theory of localization of mental systems. He goes on to utilize the analogy to establish and support his particular view of consciousness as being determined primarily by internal, unconscious instincts rather than by stimuli from the external world. He does this by pointing out that the cerebral cortex, the seat of consciousness, is shielded from excitation from the outside world by the thick skull, while there is no such protective shield between the cortex and the lower parts of the brain. Translated into the terms of the mental apparatus, this means, according to Freud, that consciousness is protected against external influence but unprotected against the feelings of pleasure and pain from the driving forces of The Unconscious.

Continuing the analogy, he describes the cerebral cortex as having only the sense organs—eyes, ears and nose—as peepholes through the skull and giving limited access to the external world. Even these peep-hole sense organs have built-in apparati for so modifying the external stimuli that Freud likens them to "feelers which are all the time making tentative advances towards the external world and then drawing back from it."[13] Translated into mental terms, this means, for Freud, that consciousness is predominantly a reception area for internal, unconscious stimuli from instinct-gratifications in the form of pleasure and pain and only secondarily a reception area for sense experience. The point of the analogy is to establish the predominance of the internal feelings of pleasure and pain over all external stimuli, and thereby "prove" the assumption that consciousness is determined primarily by instinct-presentations and only subordinately by sense experience.

The proposition that consciousness (and therefore personality, behavior and character, as well as science and art) is determined by internal and inborn instinctive forces, rather than by external and acquired sensory experience, is a central doctrine underlying all of Freud's theories. And, as we have just seen, the doctrine is supported in the first instance by a speculative *analogy* with cerebral anatomy. The proposition is so important and the process of its establishment by assumption buttressed through analogy is so patently far-fetched, that we will allow Freud, himself, to present it in its most succinct form: "The fact that the cortical layer which receives stimuli is without any protective shield against excitations from within must have as its result that these latter transmissions of stimulus have a preponderance in ecomonic importance. . . . The most abundant sources of this internal excitation are what are described as the organism's 'instincts'—the representatives of all the forces originating in the interior of the body and transmitted to the mental apparatus—at once the most important and the most obscure element of psychological research."

Such are Freud's avowedly metapsychological speculations concerning the three systems of the mental apparatus. Of his metapsychology he says, "The indefiniteness of all our discussions on what we describe as metapsychology is of course due to the fact that we know nothing of the nature of the excitatory process that takes place in the elements of the psychical systems, and that we do not feel justified in framing any hypothesis on the subject. We are consequently operating all the time with a large unknown quantity, which we are obliged to carry over into every new formula." [14] Lack of knowledge in other fields and particularly in cerebral physiology makes Freud's task all but impossible.

How do Freud's three systems compare with those of Pavlov?

Pavlov's Three Systems of Higher Nervous Activity

So far in our description of Pavlov's theory of the higher nervous activity of the cerebral hemispheres, we have dealt solely with the results of his experimental work with animals. We have seen how he differentiated two systems of nervous activity underlying animal adaptive behavior; the unconditioned reflex system and the conditioned reflex system.

From birth the innate reflexes in animals and human beings alike become inextricably interwoven with acquired and temporary sensory signals. Thus, according to Pavlov, the first and second systems are not only interrelated but mutally dependent one on the other. Every operation of an "instinct"—or chain of reflexes—acts at the same time to knit sensory signals more closely into its fabric. The outcome of the close working together of the inborn and acquired systems of higher nervous activity is a *fusion* of "instincts" with sensory signals to form *fused* reflexes.[15] With repetition, these fused reflexes are knit into systems and become what Pavlov termed *dynamic stereotypes* —what at a descriptive level are called *patterns of behavior* or *habits*. The fused reflexes, formed into dynamic stereotypes, are the combination of hereditary and acquired adaptations to environmental conditions of life. As such they are absolutely vital to the survival of animals and infant human beings. For example, the complex alimentary reflexes connected with seizing, chewing, swallowing and digesting are, almost from the moment of birth,* interwoven with "learning from experience." Sensory signals are gradually, and often painfully, acquired which break up, analyze and classify the environment into signs representing objects which are bitter or sweet, hard or soft, edible or nonedible, dangerous or friendly, and the like.

This interdependence to the point of fused reflexes of the first and second systems of higher nervous activity has a double significance in the establishment and maintenance of a dynamic equilibrium between the organism and the environment. First, the fact that the unconditioned inborn reflexes are fused with the acquired sensory signals transform the generalized, clumsy and inaccurate "instincts" into highly specific, delicate and accurate dynamic stereotypes or habits of behavior. This insures within practical limits the effectiveness of the innate reflexes, that is, it makes possible their effective functioning. Secondly, the fusion of innate and acquired reflexes, insures that the end-

---

*Recent experimental work identifies the formation of conditioned reflexes in the infant as early as one month after birth.

less welter of sensory signals will be directly or indirectly related to the vital functioning of the animal organism.

The first and second systems comprise the totality of higher nervous functioning in animals and human infants. The two functional systems, working together to form fused reflexes combined into dynamic (changeable and constantly changing) stereotypes, are capable of producing the exceedingly intricate, delicate and complex nervous activity underlying all the endless subtle modulations of animal and infant behavior. They can make animals and, of course, especialy infants, appear to behave almost with the emotional and ideational attributes of older children and even adults. One thing, however, is lacking —a condition without which, appearances to the contrary notwithstanding, there can be no *truly distinctive* human higher nervous activity or behavior. This condition is the activation of an additional system of cerebral functioning.

The third and specifically human system of higher nervous activity is, according to Pavlov, the speech or language system of signalling. Its anatomical seat is, like the sensory system, in the cerebral cortex and its mode of operation is the conditioned reflex. Words, spoken, heard and written, become conditioned stimuli, signs or signals standing for, and generalizing, the sensory signals of reality. Words are stereotyped sounds and visual images which have come, in the course of tens of thousands and hundreds of thousands of years, to represent sensory images, or abstractions from them. Words label and classify objects and actions and their more or less subtle distinctions. Thus the word *tree* stands as an abstract sign representing a generalization from all the visual images of specific trees of whatever type. It is the name for a class of things distinguished by certain sensory characteristics.

As signals, words are, on the one hand, like all other conditioned stimuli. They are subject to the general laws of the formation and extinction of conditioned reflexes, and the pinpointing of those reflexes through higher nervous analysis by means of the processes of irradiation and concentration. On the other hand, they are qualitatively different from all other conditioned stimuli. The great difference consists in their *abstract* quality. Words are applicable to *all* instances at all times.

The word "tree" stands for each and every given tree, and as a sign can evoke all the conditioned reflexes associated with the sensory signals of the actual object.

This abstract quality of words thus allows a much more *concrete* understanding of specific objects. It allows human beings to learn from the accumulated experience of mankind down the ages and from any part of the earth, and to apply this knowledge in each and every concrete instance in which the word-signal "tree," for example, is appropriate.

Conditioned *sensory* reflex signals allow animals and infants to learn from their own experience, including mimicry. This is a great step over lower forms of life, such as plants limited to tropisms or certain animals limited to tactile reactions. But compared with the tremendous flexibility of reaction that man has through the operation of the speech system, the sensory conditioned reflexes of animals and infants is *relatively* clumsy and primitive.

This becomes perfectly clear when we realize that human thought is primarily self-communication by means of language and that labor, industry, agriculture and engineering as well as both science and art are dependent on the existence of the language or speech system of signalling. In terms of historical evolution, the speech system of conditioned reflexes developed in and through and along with social living and labor, industry, agriculture, art and science, so that the third system is at once both the product of those human activities and a condition for their development.

In the course of development from infancy to childhood, the crucial transition is the acquiring of the speech system of signalling. With the activation of this third higher nervous system, we see the rise of a new level of *fused* conditioned reflexes. Words come to stand as signs representing the various fusions of sensory conditioned reflexes and unconditioned reflexes. More than that, they lead to formation of new three-way fusions. For example, a child may learn urinary sphincter control in the first place through sensory conditioned reflexes—e.g., rewards and punishment. Thus an unconditioned reflex is fused with a conditioned one. But with the development of the child's speech system of signalling he acquires a reenforcement of this fused reflex sphincter control—the social shame and ridicule heaped verbally on him by his playmates if this fused reflex fails to function effectively. Hence a dynamic stereotype, made up of a three-way fusion of unconditioned, sensory-conditioned and speech-conditioned reflexes, is formed which normally serves the human being effectively throughout his life. That is, of course, a relatively simple example of a three-system fusion of reflexes into a dynamic stereotype.

On the basis of his experimental and clinical work, Pavlov formulated a general law of the interrelation and interdependence of higher nervous systems: *In the waking, alert state the highest system plays a dominant and regulatory role in organizing higher nervous activity.* Applied to animals this law means that the sensory conditioned reflex system dominates, regulates and organizes the entire higher nervous functioning. In human beings, the speech system plays this role. In fused human reflexes and their combinations into dynamic stereotypes it is the conditioned reflexes to words that comprise the leading, regulatory and organizing component.

In the more complex phenomena such as association, consciousness and attention, the verbal system of signalling is likewise dominant.

According to Pavlov association is, in physiological terms, a temporary connection of previously unconnected stimuli. There are several types of such connections, one of which is the conditioned or temporary reflex, a connection between an indifferent stimulus and an unconditioned one. Thus association or temporary connection is a generic classification which includes the conditioned reflex but is not limited to it. In addition, an association or temporary connection is *any* cortical linking of stimuli. The mechanism of cortical linking is repeated simultaneous or consecutive couplings of stimuli while the cortex is in an excited state.

A temporary connection may on the one hand be an accidental linkage of stimuli, one resulting solely from simultanaity or sequence but not reflecting connections in the objective world; and on the other it may reflect regularly occurring and connected phenomena in the external world. The former may give rise to error and even superstition, while the latter constitutes the mechanism of learning and the acquiring of knowledge. In any case, a temporary connection exhibits the same laws of formation, extinction and refinement as a conditioned reflex. It is reflex activity displaying the processes of synthesis and analysis, irradiation and concentration, and excitation and inhibition.

The term "temporary connection" is the higher nervous counterpart of the psychological term "association."

In animals temporary connections are linkages exclusively of sensory signals. Here the phenomenon of *attention* is determined by the inborn orientation reflex and the excitation of the *strongest* stimulus and the inhibition of all simultaneously acting weaker stimuli. Thus the deer "pays attention," or reacts in an excitatory way, to the signals of danger, if they are at the moment the strongest stimuli, and "forgets," "represses" or inhibits any alimentary, reproductive or other conditioned or unconditioned stimuli which may concurrently be present.

At any given moment of waking life, it can be said that an animal is "paying attention" to the currently strongest set of stimuli and "forgetting" or "repressing" all weaker ones. But this would be to speak in subjective terms implying introspection. If one were to speak of animal *consciousness,* it could be said to consist in all the fused reflexes, linkages, and dynamic stereotypes which the animal had acquired in its life-time, and which could still be called into action on the occasion of appropriate stimuli. Rather than speaking of "animal consciousness," however, it would be scientifically more correct, perhaps, and certainly less confusing, to speak of the animal's acquired ability to react to, or adapt to, its conditions of life. *Reactibility* or *adaptability* is possibly better suited as a term for such animal phenomena.

In the human being, *associations* are sensory or verbal linkages or three-way fused reflexes, and their combination into dynamic stereotypes, organized in the waking state by the highest system, the speech system. The higher nervous activity underlying human *attention* is excitation by the currently strongest stimuli and inhibition of all concurrently weaker ones. At any moment in the life of a human being, this higher nervous activity can be correctly described as *paying attention* to one or another set of external (environmental) or internal (usually some set of ideas or emotions) stimuli. Thus *attention* is concerned with whatever chain of associations is currently strongest. The other side of attention is *repression* or inhibition, in which all weaker stimuli (external or internal) are temporarily inhibited.

Human *attention*, however, is not limited to the animal form, that is, to the currently strongest stimuli. Nor is human *repression* limited to the currently weaker stimuli. In man attention is characteristically organized and directed by the highest system, the speech system. It is closely related to *consciousness, thought and purposive* activity. These phenomena will be discussed more fully in the following chapter, but here we need to have some idea of the nervous activity underlying them.

Human individual consciousness, in the Pavlovian view, comprises all the currently operative three-way fused reflexes, linkages, and dynamic stereotypes which have been formed in the course of a person's life. Consciousness thus includes emotions and ideas and the acquired ability to make *logical* linkages or associations. The latter comprises the essence of thought. Thinking is the following through of a chain of associations according to rules of logical induction and deduction. The latter are themselves conditioned temporary connections composing stereotypes which are acquired in the course of life without any academic training in *logic*. The train of associations regulated by logical rules may be either true or false—may or may not correspond to objective reality. But in any case such an associative series is characteristic of thought. By means of such thought man can *think before he acts,* that is, he can, by means of logically governed word associations, follow through *vicariously* certain alternative courses of action, and only after he has selected the most suitable one, does he act.

Purposive activity of this kind is possible *only* in human beings because it is contingent on the thought processes which in turn depend on the higher nervous activity of the speech as well as the sensory systems. Only by means of thought can man perceive the discrepancy between the way things are and the way he would like them to be, and set up a goal to mould conditions so that they more nearly agree with his needs. He can then purposively work toward the visualized goal. Thought (thinking) underlies purposive activity, and the higher nervous activity of logically organized chains of cortical linkages underlies thought.

The *consciousness* of a person is not his immediate preoccupation. The latter is *attention*. Consciousness includes the tremendous capacity of the individual to make innumerable conditioned connections or associations. Only the associative connections now being made, at any given moment, constitute *attention*. In human beings attention is governed and directed for the most part by the purpose-at-hand, rather than by the strongest stimuli, as in animals. Of course, the purpose may be the strongest stimulus, but in any case human attention differs qualitatively from its animal counterpart by being closely connected with purposive activity.

The current purpose determines what types of stimuli I must react to, and all those stimuli which might intrude must be temporarily repressed or inhibited. Thus *attention,* activated linkages, can be likened to a searchlight which lights up a given limited area of consciousness for temporary activity. All the rest of consciousness, the possible associations and chains of associations, remain *temporarily inoperative*. Of course, fortuitous events may intrude on my purposively directed attention. Some of these can be successfully repressed, but others may temporarily make a more immediate demand on my attention than my original purpose.

In all this the distinction is not between consciousness and unconsciousness, but between consciousness as a vast conglomeration of possible but currently inactive associations or conditioned connections (based on the whole past but still potentially operative experience of the individual) and the small part of this consciousness which is at the moment in active operation. The contrast is thus between *consciousness as a whole* on the one hand and *conscious attention* on the other.

Confrontation of the Two Systems

In the foregoing juxtaposition we have for the first time a fully comparable confrontation of the theories of Pavlov and

Freud. Heretofore we have had to compare Freud's views on human higher activity with Pavlov's experimental work on dogs. Now, however, we have arrived at the point where we can make a more equal comparison, for we are beginning to examine the application of Pavlov's science of higher nervous activity to the understanding of mental phenomena.

We recall that Freud's approach was that psychology and psychiatry could not wait for other sciences, in the first place cerebral physiology, to supply the base on which to build, but rather must proceed on a purely mental plane. Pavlov's approach was the opposite, the sciences of psychology and psychiatry can make little further real progress without the base which can be supplied chiefly by the physiology and pathophysiology of the cerebral hemispheres.

We have examined these two views with regard to the general theory of the apparatus of human higher activity. We have seen that Freud, according to his own testimony, relied on conjecture, speculation and assumption and called his efforts at psychological system-building "metapsychology." After examining his attempt to reconstruct "the mental apparatus" without benefit of other sciences, we have no alternative but to agree with him: it *is* conjecture, speculation and assumption. His description of the three compound systems of the mental apparatus together with their dramatic conflicts, insubordinations and censorships may be ingenious and artistically creative, and may even be able to give *an* account of all mental phenomena, but it would be difficult for anyone to fly in the face of Freud's own testimony and call this "science." The conclusion all but forces itself: this is closer to fiction than to science. And some of it is closer to the fantastic than to fiction. Freud, himself, is led on occasion to remark, "Let us now hark back for a moment ourselves and consider whether there is any basis at all for these speculations,"[16] and "All these speculations lead nowhere" but "since we cannot wait for another science to present us with a theory" we have to proceed with the speculations.

Simply the presentation of Freud's metapsychology leads to the conclusion that it is speculation and not scientific theory— or even fruitful hypothesizing which some day might guide science. But when the "theory" of the mental apparatus is confronted by an experimentally and clinically derived theory such as Pavlov's general scheme of human higher nervous activity, the contrast is sharp and glaring.

On the one hand, Freud presents a non-material, purely mental apparatus in terms of the spatial location of a series of mental compartments, each containing ideas charged with psychic energy. All the main components of this presentation are concepts applicable solely to material objects and processes: apparatus, spatial location, and energy. It makes sense to speak of an electrical, a mechanical, a physical, chemical or nervous apparatus or compartment, but what does *mental apparatus* or *mental compartment* denote? It makes sense to speak of the spatial location of electrical, mechanical, physical, chemical or nervous processes, but what does the *spatial location of mental processes* mean? It makes sense to speak of electrical, mechanical, physical, chemical or nervous energy, but what can be denoted by *psychic energy*? In each case, Freud combines perfectly clear and scientific terms denoting material objects and processes with the term *mental* or *psychic,* thereby conjuring up an absolutely contradictory and meaningless concept. He then proceeds to treat these impossible concepts as material entities existing in time and space, with locomotion and self-propulsion. He likewise treats ideas and memories as material attributes which, among other things, can be passed on from generation to generation by means of biological heredity. Not only instincts are hereditary, but the ideas based on them, what he calls *instinct-presentations.* The *archaic heritage,* memories of tribal times, are held to be biologically transmitted. He treats ideas as entities *stored* in mental compartments of the psychic aparatus.

Throughout his metapsychology Freud employs *analogy* with material objects and processes to construct his purely mental system. This method of analogy becomes, as we have seen, patently ludicrous when he employs the spatial location of the cerebral cortex and the skull to establish his conception of the spatial location of consciousness, and its domination by internal excitation from The Unconscious, since there is no shielding skull between the cortex and the lower parts of the brain, as there is between the cortex and the outside world. Reasoning by analogy has a useful but highly restricted place in the formation of hypotheses, but when it dominates thought, the outcome can only be irrational and fantastic.

In his general theory of the human higher nervous activity, Pavlov, on the other hand, employs accepted scientific concepts of material processes—nervous apparatus or system, location of functions in parts of the brain, and nervous energy. Innate mechanisms are inborn paths of the conduction of nervous excitation along nerve tracts. Ideas, thoughts, associations are a product of conditioned reflexes to words, grammar and logic, in the form of nervous paths opened in the course of life experience. Ideas are not stored in spatial compartments, unconscious or conscious, but are potential associations made possible by already formed nerve connections awaiting only the appropriate stimuli to be once more present. Ideas are not material entities; they do not exist *anywhere,* nor do they go *somewhere* when not being thought about. They are potential or actual nervous connections or associations. When "ideas are not before the mind" they are existent only as potential connections of nerve tracts which may or may not ever again be used, depending on external sense stimuli or internal association stimuli. To speak of forgotten or repressed ideas as existing in some Unconscious or preconscious compartment of the mind is a meaningless analogy with the kind of physical entities, such as stars or molecules, which if they are not "here" must be "there." To speak of forgotten or repressed ideas as existing in some mental container and at the same time retaining their *charge of psychic energy* or *cathexis* is to compound the meaningless analogy.

Pavlov's three systems of higher nervous activity with their processes of synthesis and analysis, excitation and inhibition, irradiation and concentration are material seats of material activity, governed by objective laws of motion. The brain is a material organ functioning in and through material processes. This does not mean, as we will see in the next chapter, the reduction of mental life to material activity, but it does mean that the former cannot be explained or accounted for purely in its own terms. When such a purely *mental* explanation is attempted, the result is reasoning by speculative analogy as in the case of Freud's metapsychology.

Here again as in the case of Freud's theory of instincts confronted by Pavlov's theory of the unconditioned reflex, we have no alternative but to conclude that Pavlov's three systems provide a far more scientific basis for future work in psychology and psychiatry. As a matter of fact it is something of a distortion to put the comparison in quantitative terms. It should rather be said that Pavlov's three systems are scientific, while Freud's are essentially speculative and therefore unscientific.

But neither the self-imposed label of "speculation," nor the overwhelming nature of the comparison with Pavlov's general theory, is sufficient to form a conclusion about the validity of those of Freud's theories avowedly based on observation. Freud, himself, never put too much stock in his metapsychology and never tired of warning his readers that "these ideas are not the basis of the science upon which everything rests: that, on the contrary, is observation alone. They are not the foundation-stone, but the coping of the whole structure, and they can be replaced and discarded without damaging it."[17] Whether or not this is the case, we will be in a position to determine only at the end of this volume.

The final and conclusive test of his *working* theories lies in confronting them by more scientific, more simple and more effective theories. Freud's *working* theories are those developed out of his psychoanalytic practice, employing the technique of dream interpretation, free association and transference on such phenomena as hypnosis and hypnotic suggestion, sleep and dreams, forgetting, slips of tongue and neuroses and psychoses. All these phenomena had defied adequate scientific explanation by psychology and psychiatry and by cerebral physiology and patho-physiology. These sciences had failed to give Freud or anyone else the answers to their perfectly legitimate questions. Freud developed his own answers and they have been considered scientifically adequate by large numbers of people all over the world, professional as well as lay.

The real test, therefore, of Freud's approach to mental activity lies in the ability to give a *thoroughly scientific explanation* of the phenomena listed above. Anything short of this leaves Freud still in possession of a near monopoly in the field. No amount of castigation or ridicule will accomplish the task.

Only point by point confrontation by scientific explanation can make any real headway. Such a confrontation was begun in the present chapter. Through immediate juxtaposition we have now to confront Freud's theories of hypnosis, hypnotic suggestion, sleep and dreams by Pavlov's counterparts.

Chapter VI
SLEEP, DREAMS AND HYPNOSIS

AMONG ALL THE various one to one comparisons of Freud with Pavlov, perhaps the most striking are those concerned with hypnosis, hypnotic suggestion, sleep and dreams. It happens that the two approaches to the human mind here meet most squarely and sharply. This is decisive because of the supreme importance Freud attached especially to the nature of dreams and their interpretation. A confrontation of Freud's theories of sleep, dreams, hypnosis and hypnotic suggestion by Pavlov's concommitant theories will allow us to draw conclusions with regard to a central feature of Freud's psychoanalysis. The two sets of theories are presented in immediate juxaposition.

Freud's Theory of Hypnosis, Hypnotic Suggestion, Sleep and Dreams

Here we are concerned with Freud's analysis of four special types of phenomena, *hynosis, hypnotic suggestion, sleep and dreams*. We will recall that they are cited by Freud in evidence for the existence of the unconscious system of the mental apparatus.

1. *Freud's theory of hynosis and hypnotic suggestion*. A simple experiment in hypnotic suggestion, cited by Freud, illustrates the operation of the two higher systems of the mental apparatus, the Cs and the Pcs. A person is put into a hypnotic state and is subsequently aroused. While he was under hypnosis and under the influence of the hypnotist, he was ordered to execute a certain action at a certain fixed moment after his awakening, say half an hour later. He awakes, and seems fully conscious and in his ordinary condition; he has no recollection of his hypnotic state, and yet at the pre-arranged moment there rushes

into his mind the impulse to do the thing he was commanded to do, and he does it consciously, though not knowing why.

In his analysis of this experiment Freud holds that the order had been latently present in the (Unconscious) Pcs system of the subject's mind while under hypnosis, and at the appointed moment after awakening broke through the Pcs-Cs censorship into the Cs system. As soon as it entered the Cs, that is, became an object of attention, it was translated into motor activity. The real stimulus, however, was according to Freud, the authoritative command of the hypnotist and this remained unconscious though still very much active—that is, it retained its charge of psychic energy in the Pcs system and this cathexis was the immediate cause of the entry of the idea of the action into consciousness and its translation into motor discharge. The latter dissipated the charge of psychic energy of the unconscious (Pcs) command, and thereby ended its existence, bringing the experimental hynotic suggestion to a close.

In this way Freud describes and accounts for the simplest kind of hynotic suggestion. He *assumes* that an unconscious but active idea causes the phenomenon. "The idea of the action ordered in hypnosis," he says, "not only became an object of consciousness at a certain moment, but the more striking aspect of the fact is that this idea grew *active:* it was translated into action as soon as consciousness became aware of its presence. The real stimulus to the action being the order of the physician, it is hard not to concede that the idea of the physician's order became active too. Yet this last idea did not reveal itself to consciousness, as did its outcome, the idea of the action; it remained unconscious, and so it was *active* and *unconscious* at the same time."[1] That ideas can be active and at the same time unconscious is what Freud wants to prove in order to establish the existence of the unconscious systems of the mental apparatus. The analysis of the experiment so far implies the existence of only the higher unconscious system, the PCs. The strictly unconscious system also is involved in Freud's theory of the *mechanism* of hypnosis itself.

In his theory of how hypnosis is induced Freud already assumes not only that the Ucs exists but that it is in part made up of inborn, repressed tribal memories inherited from primitive times ages ago. This innate archaic heritage exists in The Unconscious and brings its decisive influence to bear on human behavior. The particular unconscious tribal-memory relevant for Freud's explanation of hypnosis is the repressed image of the leader of the "primal horde" whose face is terrible to behold and to whom one can only surrender one's will. It is this unconscious image that lies behind the child's submissive relation to his father—and the subject's relation to the hypnotist.

But we will let Freud present his theory of the mechanism of hypnosis in his own words: "Let us recall," he says, "that hypnosis has something positively uncanny about it; but the characteristic of uncanniness suggests something old and familiar that has undergone repression. Let us consider how hypnosis is induced. The hypnotist asserts that he is in possession of a mysterious power which robs the subject of his own will, or, which is the same thing, the subject believes it of him. This mysterious power (which is even now often described popularly as animal magnetism) must be the same that is looked upon by primitive people as the source of taboo, the same that emanates from kings and chieftains and makes it dangerous to approach them (mana). The hypnotist, then, is supposed to be in possession of this power; and how does he manifest it? By telling the subject to look him in the eyes; his most typical method of hypnotizing is by his look. But it is precisely the sight of the chieftain that is dangerous and unbearable for primitive people, just as later that of the Godhead is for mortals. . . . By the measures that he takes, then, the hypnotist awakens in the subject a portion of his archaic inheritance which had also made him compliant towards his parents and which had experienced an individual re-animation in his relation to his father; what is thus awakened is the idea of a paramount and dangerous personality, towards whom only a passive-masochistic attitude is possible, to whom one's will has to be surrendered—while to be alone with him, 'to look him in the face,' appears a hazardous enterprise." [2]

Thus the mechanism of the hypnosis, for Freud, is the unconscious transference to the person of the hypnotist of inborn, unconscious and repressed attitudes toward chieftains, tribal gods, and fathers. The attitudes transferred are those of danger, masochism and surrender. The act of looking into the hypnotist's eyes awakens the repressed Ucs tribal and childhood memories, the psychic cathected force of which breaks through the pre-conscious censorship and becomes a dominant but unconscious Pcs influence in the hypnotic situation. It is this unconscious memory which lends its powerful charge of psychic energy to the command of the hypnotist thereby making its execution irresistible.

Freud notes a similarity between *hypnosis* and *sleep*. At the beginning of hypnosis, the hypnotist often gives the *command* to sleep. When he does this, he is, according to Freud, putting himself in the place of the father. If he *coaxes* the subject to sleep, he is putting himself in the place of the mother. In either case, he puts himself in the place of the subject's parents with all their borrowed cathected heritage of Ucs tribal memories of chieftains and tribal gods. Thus the command or coaxing to sleep is reenforced by The Unconscious.

The instruction to sleep in hypnosis means, according to Freud, to withdraw all interest from the external world and to concentrate it on the person of the hypnotist. The "withdrawal of interest from the outer world" is considered by Freud to be the primary condition for sleep. "In this withdrawal of interest from the outer world," he says, "lies the psychological characteristic of sleep, and the kinship between sleep and the state of hypnosis is based upon it."[3]

2. *Freud's theory of sleep and dreams*. Freud points out that every night human beings lay aside the garments they pull over their skin, and also other objects which they use to supplement their bodily organs and those they use as substitutes for their deficiences—for instance, their spectacles, false hair or teeth, and so on. "In addition to this," he says, "when they go to sleep they perform a perfectly analogous dismantling of their minds—they lay aside most of their mental acquisitions; thus both physically and mentally approaching remarkably close to the situation in which they began life." Somatically, according to Freud, sleep is a *regression* to an earlier state, a return as far as possible to the pre-natal, intra-uterine, foetal state. Psychologically he regards sleep as a regression to earlier states, specifically to a state which he characterizes as *primitive narcis-*

sim and as *hallucinatory wish-fulfillment.* As a regression to primitive narcissim, sleep signifies psychologically that the person has withdrawn all interest from the external world and concentrated it on himself. But primitive narcissim implies also, for Freud, a libidinal or sexual love of self—treating one's own self as a sexual object.

As we will see in the following chapter, narcissism is viewed by Freud as a stage in the early character development of the child. In sleep, an adult regresses as far as possible toward infantile narcissism. He calls this "the narcissism of sleep" and considers it to be the first of two primary mental characteristics of sleep. *The narcissism of sleep* is egoism with libidinal or sexual content. "Narcissism," Freud says, "may be described as the libidinal complement of egoism." In sleep the ego withdraws away from the world into itself in the form of a more or less sexual self-love.

How does Freud know this? "It is, of course, the study of dreams," he says, "which has taught us what we know of the mental characteristics of sleep." Thus in dreams it is always the person dreaming who plays the chief part in their scenes, and the scenes, according to Freud, are almost always at least ultimately sexual in content—hence "the narcissism of sleep." [4]

The other mental characteristic of sleep, *hallucinatory wish-fulfillment,* is likewise the product of Freud's interpretation of dreams. With the withdrawal of the ego's interest in the external world and its concentration in libidinal self-love (primitive narcissism), all the instinct-stimuli from the various organs of the body are greatly magnified and tend to disturb sleep. The instinct-stimuli excite the repressed instinct presentations in The Unconscious, adding greatly to their cathexes. It is these heightened repressed instinct cathexes, and particularly the sexual or libidinal ones, which threaten to disturb sleep by forcing their way through the censorship into the Pcs system and thence into the Cs system which would in turn awaken the sleeper. Among other things, the state of sleeping involves not only a *heightening* of the unconscious repressed ideas and their cathexes, but also a *lowering* of the vigilance of the censorship. These two factors combine to produce a threat to sleep.

The mental apparatus, however, has a defense against the disturbance of sleep from internal Ucs pressure and this defense mechanism is the second primary mental characteristic of sleep, namely, hallucinatory wish-fulfillment. Freud calls the defense mechanism of hallucinatory wish-fulfillment *projection*. Projection is, according to him, a particular way of dealing with internal excitations from the Ucs system which are too strong for the censorship and which cause great unpleasure or pain when they succeed in breaking through into the Pcs and Cs systems. The particular way of dealing with them is "to treat them as though they were acting, not from the inside, but from the outside." [5]

By such a *projection*, the disturbing clamor of the unconscious wish-impulse threatening sleep is transformed in dreams into the instinctive wish-impulse as already satisfied through motor discharge. "A dream," Freud says, "indicates that something was going on which tended to disturb sleep, and it enables us to understand the way in which this disturbance can be warded off. The final outcome is that the sleeper has dreamed and is able to go on sleeping; the inner claim which wanted to absorb him has been replaced by an outer experience, the claim of which he has succeeded in discharging. A dream is therefore, among other things, a projection: an externalization of an internal process." [6]

The dream protects sleep, then, by presenting Ucs wish-impulses as already fulfilled, and thereby sleep may continue. Perhaps the simplest example cited by Freud are dreams resulting from a full bladder. The wish-impulse to urinate, derived from this bodily organ, threatens to disturb sleep. Sleep may be preserved by a dream projecting this internal excitation as an external act of urination already accomplished. The sleeper may then go on sleeping.

In addition to the somatic function of guarding sleep, dreams have, according to Freud, a mental function. The mental function of dreams is, he holds, to provide one of the circuitous routes allowing repressed unconscious impulses to enter the Pcs and Cs systems in disguised forms. The mechanism of this mental function of dreams involves what Freud calls *the manifest dream material* and *the latent dream* content. The manifest dream material furnishes the disguise concealing from the censorship the latent dream content. The pre-conscious dresses the Ucs wish-impulse (the latent dream content) in a masquerade costume composed of Pcs memory-traces of events of the preceding day (the manifest dream material). The manifest dream material is what the dreamer remembers upon waking. Only psychoanalytic dream interpretation can disclose, by means of symbol translation with the aid of free association, the *meaning* of the dream, namely its latent dream content—the Ucs wish-impulses concealed beneath the vivid dream imagery of recent, commonplace daily happenings.

Freud accounts for the generally recognized phenomena of dreams—the imagery, the paucity of verbal ideas, the lack of logic and coherence, and the irrationality—primarily by his conception of the unconscious system (Ucs) and secondarily by the pre-conscious system (Pcs). There can be no question about the authenticity of the dream phenomena he cites. The real question is how to account for them. Freud does it on a purely mental basis, in terms of his conjectural three-systems of the mental apparatus.

PAVLOV'S THEORY OF SLEEP, DREAMS, HYPNOSIS AND HYPNOTIC SUGGESTION

From his experimental work with animals and from his work in the psychiatric clinic Pavlov concluded that *sleep* is an irradiating inhibition which is not effectively checked by the opposite process of excitation. Not all inhibition is full sleep, but all sleep is unchecked irradiating inhibition. "Inhibition," Pavlov says, "is a partial, fragmentary, narrowly limited, strictly localised sleep, confined within definite boundaries under the influence of the opposing process—that of excitation; sleep on the contrary is an inhibition which has spread over a great section of the cerebrum, over the entire hemispheres and even into the lower lying mid-brain. . . . Either the inhibition spreads and sleep sets in, or the inhibition is limited and sleep disappears." [7]

There are two sets of stimuli which induce the irradiating inhibition of sleep: the internal stimuli of *fatigue* and all monotonously repetitious external stimuli or the equally monotonous lack of stimuli. We go to bed when the internal fatigue stimuli become irresistible; but even then sleep inhibition may be checked because of various excitatory thought stimuli, perhaps in the form of worries, problems, etc. Popular tradition then tells us to add monotonous stimuli such as "counting sheep." In many cases this will counteract excitation and allow the irradiating inhibition to spread unhampered. In some cases, neither fatigue stimuli nor monotonous stimuli are effective, and "sleepless nights" result.

The adaptive function of sleep is to overcome fatigue (a certain metabolic state of the nerve cells of the brain and particularly of the cerebral hemispheres leading to reduced excitability), by *rest* and consequent *restoration* of cellular reactivity (restoring the alert metabolic state of these cells). There is, Pavlov maintains, no special *sleep center* in the brain because, as he says, "inhibition and sleep exist for each cell. Consequently, they do not need any special cellular group." [8]

During roughly two-thirds of each twenty-four hour day the three systems of higher nervous activity in each of us is a constantly changing, dynamic equilibrium between the excitatory and inhibitory processes—excitations set in and irradiate until they are checked by inhibition and are thereby transformed into concentration. Connections are made, broken and analyzed and in this way we carry on our thoughtful and purposeful activities of work, vital functions and recreation. During the remaining third of the day, customarily at night, this equilibrium is broken and inhibition takes more or less full charge. This eight-hour, almost unrestricted domination of the higher nervous activity by irradiating inhibition is the *condition* for the next sixteen-hours of active, waking life—including all the highest manifestations of human activity; productive labor, science, art, social living and family life; the internal dynamic equilibrium of the individual person and the external dynamic equilibrium with the environment. All this is dependent on the healthy functioning of the three systems of higher nervous activity in each of us. The primary insurance for this nervous health is sleep; thus in a very real sense the highest manifestations of human life depend on the *inactive* state of the nerve cells of the brain and particularly of the cerebral hemispheres.

As unchecked, irradiating inhibition, sleep comes, not all at once, but more or less gradually. Human sleep is an inhibition which, according to Pavlov, originates in the highest part of the cerebral hemispheres and spreads gradually over the entire hemispheres and down into the lower levels of the brain. The highest part of the cerebral cortex is that which controls *verbal activity,* namely the seat of the speech (or second signalling) system. Thus the speech system is the first system to pass at least partially into the inactive state of irradiating inhibition, or sleep. When this happens, and it happens every time we "fall asleep," it immediately breaks the dynamic equilibrium between the three systems of higher nervous activity. It causes, to a greater or lesser degree, a *dissociation* of the three systems—the *fused* reflex functioning is disrupted.

Since the fusion of reflexes is organized and regulated by the speech system, the partial withdrawal (through inhibition) of this system leaves the sensory and unconditioned reflex systems more or less disorganized and unregulated. Thus in the relatively brief transition from the waking state to full sleep, there is a period of time when the two lower systems function without full organization and control by the highest. This, together with the corresponding transition period of "waking up," is the period in which we *dream*. Thus, according to Pavlov, *dreams* are the product of the particular dissociation of the three systems of higher nervous activity characteristic of the transitional periods between the onset of sleep and full sleep and between full sleep and the waking state. This, by the way, is in accord with the popular notion that one dreams when one is either falling asleep or waking up.

The main features of dreams, their vivid sensory images and their chaotic and illogical character, are the direct result of the inhibition of the speech system and the concomitant "liberation" of the two lower systems, especially the sensory system, from organization and regulation by the speech system of signalling. In dreams, all kinds of memory traces arise and weird connections are made, which would never occur in the waking state under the control of the highest system. Hence comes the amusing and sometimes shocking and even terrifying elements in dreams.

Dreams are, thus, primarily the product of the dislocated, dissociated functioning of the cerebral hemispheres. As such they are not so much features of the nervous processes underlying normal mental activity, as they are transitory physiological phenomena characteristic of a certain phase of falling asleep and awakening. This view, too, is fully in accord with the popular notion that dreams do not *really mean* anything and are therefore better ignored. This does not, however, signify that it is impossible, for example, to get a new idea from thinking over dream material. The connection of certain sensory images might occur which would give one an idea which had not previously occurred to one. But this would be largely fortuitous and would ultimately depend on the experiences of the more or less recent past, particularly of the day before.

Another phenomenon, characteristic of sleep and related to hypnotic suggestion (as we will soon see), is what Pavlov calls the *nocturnal sentinel*. When irradiating inhibition spreads over the cerebral hemispheres and sleep sets in, certain points within the hemispheres, which are called "points on duty" or "points on guard," may remain active. These more or less isolated points remain alert to certain types of stimuli, with the function of protecting the organism, or the offspring, or in certain cases, as part of a job to be done. They are, of course, the product of conditioning or training. Examples are: In the sleep of an animal which wakes up immediately at the weakest signal of the presence of an enemy, or even of anything strange; in the sleep of a lighthouse keeper who wakes up when the fog-horn stops; in the sleep of a mother who wakes up at the faintest sound coming from her child, but who is not disturbed by much louder sounds. Thus the *nocturnal sentinel* is a critical "point" which remains in *rapport* with certain determinate stimuli; but not with others.

The phenomenon of the nocturnal sentinel is related, as was mentioned above, to hypnotic suggestion. *Hypnosis* is, according to Pavlov, a kind of irradiating inhibition or sleep which gradually spreads from a *basic point* in the cerebral cortex. This basic point is the reception area for the monotonous gestures and tones of the hypnotist. As the inhibition spreads this point of origin remains on guard or on duty as an active point in *rapport* with the hypnotist. Rapport, in this sense, signifies the special faculty of a hypnotized person for perceiving in a selective way exclusively the words of the hypnotist without maintaining any contact with the rest of the external world. The mechanism is very similar to the nocturnal sentinel. Since the excitatory process in the entire cortex is very weak, due to the partial or hypnotic sleep, all the excitation of which the hypnotized cortex is capable concentrates on the one stimulus (the suggestion or command) entering at the cortical point which remains active. There is nothing left for other stimuli and they remain inactive. When the order is given the hypnotist has everything extremely restricted so that there can be no opposition to it. The hypnotized person inevitably executes the order or follows the suggestion, for when he wakes up he is powerless to do anything with this *isolated excitation, since it is wholly detached* from all others.[9]

Hypnotic suggestion is viewed by Pavlov, then, as a physiological process which, like dreams, is not a "normal" mental phenomenon, but a peculiarity of higher nervous activity in a dissociated state.

Confrontation

Since dreams are most decisive for Freud, we begin the evaluation with the two theories of dreams.

In his *Interpretation of Dreams,* Freud reviews many theories, accepting essential elements from all but two. "We have been compelled," he says, "to take decided exception to two only of the views expressed; namely, that the dream is a meaningless process, and that it is a somatic process."

Pavlov was not by any means the first to treat dreams as primarily "somatic" or physiological processes. As a matter of fact physiology, medicine, and science generally have for centuries viewed dreams in this way. Freud, himself, remarks that the physiological somatic theory is "by far the most favored by medical writers, and by scientists in general." Most of the physiological theories of dreams hold them to be phenomena characteristic of the transition from sleep to waking and waking to sleep. Pavlov's contribution consists in the elaboration of the theory in terms of the *dissociation* of the sensory and speech systems of signalling in the transitional phases of sleep and waking. This is a big step over the older physiological theories which were by and large limited to ascribing dreams to the isolated work of groups of waking cerebral cells surrounded by sleeping cells. The fact that the earlier physiological theories were more the product of scientific conjecture than of a developed science of higher nervous activity, allowed Freud to discount them and proceed to construct a purely mental theory. Here again the lack of a physiology of the cerebral hemispheres paved the way for Freud's speculation.

Pavlov's physiological theory of dreams, an integral part of his experimentally and clinically derived science of higher nervous activity, goes a long way toward filling the gap in knowledge which led to Freud's fantastic theory. The tale of the unconscious and repressed wish-impulses insubordinately defying the ego's wish to withdraw all cathexes from the external and internal world, and then, taking advantage of a lowering of the censorship in sleep, bursting into dream activity under the disguise of pre-conscious day-residues, *is* certainly fantastic. It is an ingenious, if laborious and overly complicated, attempt to fill an hiatus in knowledge. But once that hiatus is overcome the speculative makeshift appears, like astrology confronted by astronomy, as a rather clumsy myth. Like astrology, the only basis for mythical theories is ignorance. Myths are, and always have been, a substitute for knowledge. Ignorance appears to be a vacuum into which impatient, "scientists" often rush.

What is true of Freud's theory of dreams holds likewise for his theories of sleep, hypnosis and hypnotic suggestion. Freud's *narcissism of sleep,* the recall of all cathexes and their concentration in the libidinal self-love of the ego, is hardly a less ingenious, laborious and overly-complicated theoretical substitute for scientific knowledge than his theory of dreams. Its mythical character becomes fully apparent when set in immediate juxtaposition with Pavlov's physiological theory of sleep.

Freud's theories of hypnosis and hypnotic suggestion—the transference of unconscious hereditary memories of tribal chieftains and of infantile repressed fears of the father onto the person of the hypnotist, investing him with irresistible authority to command sleep and order post-hypnotic actions—are, if anything, more literally mythical than his theories of sleep and dreams. Compared with Pavlov's theory of hypnosis as partial sleep and his explanation of hypnotic suggestion in terms of the established mechanism of the sentinel, Freud's tale of the *archaic heritage* comes with the impact of a slap in the face.

Ignorance, the current lack of available scientific knowledge, is the source of myth-making speculation. But ignorance is no excuse. It should, rather, pose a challenge to patient, careful scientific work, proceeding step by step in the neverending task of conquering, one after another, the small and large gaps in human knowledge. Freud, at least with regard to sleep and dreams, hypnosis and hypnotic suggestion, tried to *leap* the gaps, a form of mental gymnastics.

We see that in these working theories the metapsychological myth-making plays an essential and inextricable role: Take away the speculative assumptions and there is no theory left.

We *may* be on the verge of concluding that Freud's concept of unconscious mental activity (the Ucs and Pcs systems of his mental apparatus) is a poor substitute for the physiology of the cerebral hemispheres, for the science of higher nervous activity. We are not yet in a position to draw such a sweeping conclusion. This, if it is to be drawn at all, must wait upon examination, in the following two chapters, of other elements in the psychoanalytical approach to mental life and mental illness.

Chapter VII

THE PSYCHOLOGICAL LINEAGE OF FREUD AND PAVLOV

AN ILLUMINATING ELEMENT in the confrontation of the Freudian and Pavlovian approaches to psychology is a comparison of the two lines of theoretical descent. The contrast in the respective forbears is a measure of the difference between psychoanalysis and a psychology based on the science of higher nervous activity. We present first Freud's and then Pavlov's approach to the problems of psychology as viewed from the historical vantage point of their intellectual lineage.

FREUD'S APPROACH TO PSYCHOLOGY

In his attempt to solve in purely psychological terms the essential problems of psychology Freud drew on the resources of at least seven currents of nineteenth century thought: hypnotic suggestion; dream symbolism, translation and interpretation; mythology; the notion of an innate archaic mental heritage; sexology; the psychology of The Unconscious; and finally, biological voluntarism and the philosophy of The Unconscious. We turn now to a discussion of Freud's theoretical line of descent.

Freud's Theoretical Lineage

Freud was attracted to the seven currents of thought through his recognition of the for-the-most-part neglected fact that much of man's mental life takes place beyond the limits of self-conscious awareness. Since there was as yet no adequate physiology of the cerebral hemispheres which could account for this *unconscious* activity, he perforce sought answers wherever they could be found.

While still a medical student Freud had attended a public exhibition of hypnotism and hypnotic suggestion by the famous nineteenth century 'personal magnetist,' Hansen, and had been deeply impressed. One of the persons Hansen had put under hypnosis had become deathly pale at the onset and had remained so as long as the hypnotic condition lasted. This convinced Freud of the genuineness of hypnotic phenomena, in spite of the prevalent opinion of the professors of psychiatry that hypnotism and hypnotic suggestion were not only fraudulent but dangerous, an erroneous opinion that persisted well into the twentieth century.[1]

Hypnotic suggestion as developed by Bernheim and Liebault, among others, convinced Freud not only that unconscious memories exist but also that human mental activity as a whole is largely unconscious with only a small part being conscious—somewhat like an iceberg the main bulk of which lies beneath the surface of the ocean.

Hypnotic suggestion demonstrated to Freud's satisfaction the importance and wide scope of unconscious mental activity. But it could not serve adequately to reveal in what the unconscious activity consisted. He solved this problem to his own satisfaction by borrowing from an occult current of thought which was, and still is, rejected and held in utter contempt by all science, the interpretation of dreams by means of symbol translation. This current of thought was available to him in the popular dream-books and more impressively in the theories of such writers as K. A. Scherner, P. Radestock, G. H. Schubert and Artemidorus. In his own book, *The Interpretation of Dreams,* Freud acknowledges his great debt to Artemidorus' *The Symbolism of Dreams* (1881), Schubert's *Symbolism of Dreams* (1814), Radestock's *Sleep and Dreams* (1878) and especially to Scherner's *The Life of Dreams* (1861). All of these works "ascribe to the dreaming mind," as Freud put it, "the capacity for and propensity to special psychic activities, which in the waking state it is able to exert either not at all or imperfectly." And they propose to uncover the content and nature of these special psychic activities primarily by means of symbol translation. They convinced Freud of two things: First that "a phantastic symbolizing activity remains as the central force of every dream"; and second, that one must seriously investigate "whether many of these symbols have not a permanently established meaning, like the signs in shorthand."[2]

The question of dream symbols and their stereotoyped meanings was a crucial one for Freud, and he proceeded at once to carry out the necessary investigations. These investigations led him from dreams to folklore, myths, legends, proverbs and current popular witticisms. He turned to mythology for help and especially to such sources as J. G. Frazer's *Golden Bough,* S. Reinich's *Cults, Myths and Religions,* and F. Max-Mueller's *Contributions to the Science of Mythology.* From this study he concluded "that symbolism does not appertain especially to dreams, but rather to the Unconscious imagination, and particularly to that of the people, and it is to be found in a more developed condition in folklore, myths, legends, idiomatic phrases, proverbs, and current witticisms of a people than in dreams."[3] But this still did not answer the question of the permanently established meaning of symbols, it merely extended the range of unconscious mental symbols beyond the limits of dreams.

He finally found what he was looking for in a non-scientific, purely descriptive and speculative book on social psychology, Gustave Le Bon's *The Psychology of Crowds* (1895).[4] Le Bon, held in complete contempt by modern psychology, maintained that what differentiates people as individuals is only an acquired mental superstructure built over an hereditary unconscious substructure identical in all people. This sub-structure exists in the form of a *racial* unconscious, an innate archaic mental heritage composed of tribal memories, impulses, drives and instincts. This archaic heritage, inborn in each of us, Le Bon held, controls our thoughts and our actions, furnishing deep and hidden motives for all we think, feel, say and do. Freud quotes the following from Le Bon's book published in 1895 and therefore antedating by one year his "discovery" of psychoanalysis: "Unconscious phenomena play an altogether preponderating part not only in organic life, but also in the operations of the intelligence. The conscious life of the mind is of small importance in comparison with its unconscious life. . . . Our conscious acts are the outcome of an unconscious substratum created in the mind in the main by hereditary influences. This substratum consists of the innumerable common characteristics handed down from generation to generation, which constitute the genius of a race. . . . The greater part of our daily actions are the result of hidden motives which escape our observation." [5] This archaic mental heritage from the race reveals itself in symbolic form in myths, folklore and dreams and constitutes the essential reason why unconscious symbols are stereotyped. They form at least in part an innate mental legacy from primitive tribal times in which object and symbol were verbally and conceptually related. Freud concluded from this "that particular psychical contents, such as symbolism, have no other source than hereditary transmission, and research in various fields of social psychology (Le Bon) seems to justify the assumption that there are other, no less specialized, deposits from primitive human development present in our archaic heritage." [6]

Here is his attempt to establish the permanent meaning of symbols by means of inborn hereditary "psychical contents," Freud is in fact reinstating the doctrine of *innate* ideas long ago rejected by John Locke as theoretically and scientifically untenable and as politically reactionary. Lock's rejection of innate ideas and his substitution of the principle that all ideas come from experience in the course of individual life was accepted and established by science over a period of two hundred and fifty years.

So far we have seen that Freud relied in the first instance on hypnotic suggestion to indicate the *existence* of unconscious mental activity, and on a dream and myth language of stereotyped symbols to reveal, upon translation, the *contents* of the unconscious mind.

The next step was to make an exhaustive study of the stereotyped symbols allegedly employed in dreams and myths. This Freud did, and he found that by far the great majority of unconscious symbols could be interpreted as having an "established" direct or indirect *sexual* meaning. The interpretive method by which Freud assigns sexual meaning to alleged stereotyped unconscious symbols is illustrated in the following excerpt from a paper written by him in 1910: "First of all there is the matter of symbolism in dreams and in the Unconscious—a fiercely contested subject, as you know! ... I will say a few words about one of the symbols that has lately been recognized. Not long ago it came to my knowledge that a psychiatrist whose views are not too distant from ours had remarked to one of us that we undoubtedly overestimate the hidden sexual significance of dreams; his most frequent dream was of going upstairs, and there could certainly be nothing sexual about that. Our attention being thus drawn to it, we began to study the incidence of stairs, steps and ladders in dreams, and soon could establish the fact that stairs and such things are certainly a symbol of coitus. The underlying element which the two things have in common is not difficult to discover; one climbs an acclivity in rhythmic movements, accompanied by increasing breathlessness, and in a few rapid leaps can be down below again. Thus the rhythm of coitus reappears in climbing steps. We will not forget to adduce the usages of speech in this connection. It shows us that 'mounting' is used quite simply as a symbol for the sexual act." [7]

Here we see that Freud's method is to take those commonly occurring images appearing in dreams, myths, folklore, etc. and subject them to a process of inferential *reasoning by analogy*. Reasoning by analogy has over the centuries been carefully hedged in and circumscribed as to its legitimacy—*limited to the preliminary stages of the formation of tentative working hypotheses, and never to proof*. Freud, however, employs the method to establish once and for all what is without doubt the most crucial element of his psychoanalytic methodology, the permanently established sexual meaning of the alleged stereotyped symbols of myths, dreams, folklore, witticisms and the like. Freud did not *find* that unconscious symbols were sexual in meaning. *He forced them to yield a sexual meaning* by subjecting them to reasoning by analogy.

With this "key" to unlock the hidden secrets of The Unconscious, Freud proceeded to analyze his patients. Utilizing the symbolic language used in reporting their dreams, and in freely associating on them, he naturally found that their unconscious minds were replete with hidden sexual impulses, numerous and age-old primitive instincts and drives and patterns of behavior. Dream images, viewed as stereotyped sexual symbols, when connected in the dream or in free associations with mother, brother, sister or with members of the same sex inevitably led Freud to infer that the patient had unconscious hidden motives, desires and impulses of an incestuous or a homosexual character. His case histories became at once so entangled in a mesh of sexual aberrations that he was impelled to make a thorough study of *sexology*. For this purpose he turned to such authorities on the subject as Krafft-Ebing, Havelock Ellis, Moebius, Schrenk-Notzing, Löwenfeld, Magnus Hirschfield, and especially to the *Yearbook of Sexual Aberrations*, published in Berlin. These studies reenforced his sexual orientation and allowed him greatly to expand his ever-growing list of stereotyped sexual symbols. This particular work was early carried forward by several of his associates, notably by Wilhelm Stekel. Soon there was a vast collection of "permanently established" symbols of unconscious sexual mental life.

In the work of tracing unconscious memories and impulses back further and further in the lives of his patients, Freud, by means of the stereotyped sexual symbols, inevitably came upon the notion of the sex life of infants and children, including incipient "aberrations," and developed it into his theory of *infantile sexuality*, with its oral, anal and genital phases, its "incestuous" Oedipus phase, and its castration complex and penis envy.

With all this, however, Freud's biggest problem remained to be solved: How does it happen that sexual memories, impulses and drives are so predominantly unconscious and why do they indicate their existence primarily in the guise of the symbolic language of dreams, myths and the like? To help solve this problem Freud had readily available the currently popular and, in Germany and Austria at the time (around 1896), the widely accepted *psychology of the unconscious*, evolved by J. F. Herbart and G. T. Fechner, and popularized by W. Griesinger.

Herbart (1776-1841) was the most influential German psychologist in the first half of the nineteenth century. Reacting against the extreme rationalism of the currently dominant Hegelian school of philosophy, he developed an approach to mind in which unconscious ideas, highly charged with energy, dominate mental life. He viewed mind as the scene of a never-ending conflict between variously energized ideas, in which the notion of *suppression* or *repression* plays a central role. An idea is suppressed or repressed *(verdrängt)* when it is blocked from reaching consciousness by some more highly charged idea or when it has been driven out of consciousness by such an idea.

Further, Herbart conceived of mind as having two *thresholds* (comparable to Freud's censors). One, called the "static threshold," separates de-energized ideas from consciousness (comparable to Freud's pre-conscious) and the other, called the "mechanistic threshold," separates those repressed or suppressed ideas, which retain their charges of energy, from the de-energized ideas and from consciousness (comparable to Freud's Unconscious). The charged unconscious ideas are, according to Herbart, in perpetual rebellion against the conscious ideas, and this sharp conflict furnishes the dynamics of mental life. The charged unconscious ideas are viewed as being capable of producing indirect effects such as "objectless feelings of oppression."

Herbart maintained that there is no such thing as absolute forgetting. Ideas are eternal. Once in the mind always in the mind. Forgetting, according to him, thus means repression. The real determinant of human thought and behavior consists in unconscious repressed ideas that remain at the same time highly energized. The main task of psychology is "to recognize from what is experienced [in consciousness] the traces of what is stirring and acting behind the curtains."

Some seventy years before Freud's "discovery" of psychoanalysis, Herbart had thus made a rough sketch of The Unconscious and a preliminary outline of the theory of repression.

There can be no question about Freud's familiarity with the Herbartian psychology. The textbook used in the Gymnasium at the time he was in attendance was strictly limited to Herbart's teachings; Freud's own teacher, Theodore Meynert, was strongly influenced by Herbart, and finally Freud, himself, made a careful study of Fechner who in turn was a follower of Herbart. It was Fechner, by the way, who first made the famous analogy likening the human mind to an iceberg which is nine-tenths submerged under water and whose course is determined not only by the wind that plays over the surface but also by the hidden currents of the ocean depths.

In Herbart's concept of repression *(Verdrängung)* with its unconscious but still highly active and rebellious ideas, Freud found the basis for his solution of the problem of why The Unconscious speaks mainly in the language of symbols. He had only to identify the unconscious and the conscious energized ideas which were in conflict, and he was in possession of the central doctrine of psychoanalysis—the theory of repression.

He was already convinced that unconscious ideas and impulses were essentially sexual in character. What ideas were opposed to admitting sexual ideas, including aberrations, to consciousness? It was a relatively simple step to assume that ideas of social, moral and religious standards, charged with all the energy of public opinion and the power of church and state, served as the conscious repressing agents. The alleged symbolic language of dreams and myths, witticisms and proverbs, folklore and idioms, was, then, the subterfuge to which rebellious, unconscious, sexual ideas resorted in order to pass the threshold or censorship and gain entrance to consciousness. Those stereotyped symbols which had become hereditary were the product of ages of repression of socially, morally and religiously non-acceptable sexual ideas. *Unrepressed* primitive human nature thus took revenge on *repressed* "civilized" human nature through the medium of the unconscious symbolic representation of the archaic, largely sexual, innate mental heritage. It did this in dreams, myths and their like, and as we will see, in neurotic and psychotic symptoms.

Making an eclectic combination of six trends, predominantly outside the main currents of nineteenth century thought—hypnotic suggestion (Hansen, Liébault and Bernheim); the interpretation of dreams by means of stereotyped symbol translations (Scherner, Radestock, Schubert, Artemidorus and popular dream books); mythology (Frazer, Reinach and Max-Mueller); archaic innate mental heritage (Le Bon); sexology (Ellis, Krafft-Ebing and the *Journal of Sexual Aberrations);* and finally the psychology of The Unconscious (Herbart and Fechner)—Freud developed his depth psychology of purely mental dynamics.

The principal notion underlying Freud's system is the essential determination of conscious life by unconscious and highly energized, instinctive ideas and impulses. Thus he stresses the unconscious affective and volitional side of mental activity with the driving force being viewed as biological rather than social. It is an irrational, anti-rational psychology, making innate emotions, impulses, instincts and drives primary to, and dominant over socially acquired ideas, thought, knowledge and rational activity. As such it is in sharp contrast and opposition to the scientific temper of the main streams of scientific thought. The Freudian psychology of the repressed unconscious, therefore, required philosophical justification and rationalization.

It so happened that a suitable trend, itself operating largely outside the classical main currents of philosophical thought, had for some time been evolving. This trend includes a wide variation of philosophical systems but has one negative and one positive characteristic in common. The common negative characteristic is a dedicated and in some instances a violent *opposition to* the *rationalism* of traditional main line philosophies whether idealist or materialist. Traditional rational philosophies have always held, among other things, that the most essential features of the human mind are reason, logic, thought, ideas, knowledge and truth.

The common positive characteristic of the modern, anti-rational trend in philosophy is *the substitution,* in the place of the rational elements, *of unconscious, biological strivings, drives, appetites, desires, emotions, impulses, intuitions, instincts, immediate practical activity and will* as the most essential features of the human mind. It is, in short, the substitution of the *affective* aspect in the place of the *rational* aspect of mind. Instincts, drives, emotions are assigned the dominant and decisive, the leading and organizing role in this philosophical trend. The trend has taken many forms, stressing now biological will, now unconscious appetition, here instincts and emotions, there immediate practical activity. It has gone under many names, voluntarism, vitalism, philosophy of the unconscious, pragmatism, "humanism," "naturalism," the philosophy of "as if" and instrumentalism, among others.[8] Many famous modern philosophers are its exponents: Arthur Schopenhauer (1788-1860); Frederick Nietzsche (1844-1900); William James (1842-1910); Eduard von Hartmann (1842-1906); Henri Bergson (1859-1941);

John Dewey (1859-1953); F. C. S. Schiller (1864-1937); and Hans Vaihinger (1852-1933).

This philosophical trend lent, and continues to lend, support in a very general way to Freud's depth psychology. It had already *downgraded* consciousness and reason, and thus had served to break the ground for psychoanalysis.

Freud, according to his own testimony, deliberately avoided contact with philosophy proper. While he did not read either Schopenhauer or Nietzsche until late in his life, their thinking was certainly familiar to him from indirect sources. He knew that the trend in philosophy of which these two philosophers were the most illustrious exponents was very close to his own point of view. As a matter of fact, it was on this very account that he avoided them. "The large extent to which psychoanalysis coincides with the philosophy of Schopenhauer—not only did he assert the dominance of the emotions and the supreme importance of sexuality but he was even aware of the mechanism of repression—is not to be traced to my acquaintance with his teaching. I read Schopenhauer very late in my life. Nietzsche, another philosopher whose guesses and intuitions often agree in the most astonishing way with the laborious findings of psychoanalysis, was for a long time avoided by me on that very account; I was less concerned with priority than with keeping my mind unembarrassed." [9]

Such is Freud's line of theoretical descent, and such are the sources on which he drew to construct his view of the human mind, his approach to psychology.

Pavlov's Approach to Psychology

Four main historical currents of psychological thought together with the materialist philosophy of science unite in the Pavlovian approach to psychology; the associationist, the physiological, the experimental and the evolutionary. Pavlov's science of the higher nervous activity of the cerebral hemispheres comprises an experimental integration and transformation of all four of those essential trends in the light of monistic materialism.

The Theoretical Lineage of Pavlov's Approach to Psychology

The underlying problem in psychology, as in philosophy, has always been the relation of body and mind. Classically there were two opposite solutions, the reduction of body to mind in the form of embodied ideas and of mind to body in the form of infinitesimal matter in motion. According as to whether the philosopher-psychologist took the first or the second position he was either an idealist or a materialist.

Idealism, usually in a theological form, was, however, the dominant solution of the body-mind problem from Plato to the scholastics of the feudal period. The materialist solution, from Democritus, Epicurus and Lucretius to Thomas Hobbes, was in many instances an element in the intellectual ferment centering around great popular movements directed against entrenched and oppressive authority. The latter traditionally employed the idealist reduction of body to mind as an element of its ideology, in support of the doctrines and myths buttressing its rule. Thus the materialist solution of the body-mind problem historically formed a part of the ideological protest against oppression.

In the modern period, as a theoretical counterpart of the epochal social and political struggles against fuedalism, the first great *decisive* theoretical step in opposition to scholasticism was made by Descartes (1596-1650), but at the expense of psychology. He made a complete division between body and mind, each being viewed as a separate substance governed by its own laws. This freed the physical sciences from the scholastic doctrine that mind permeated all of nature. It paved the way, that is, for a materialist and scientific approach to astronomy, physics and chemistry, but it did so by a grand compromise which left *mind* as the exclusive domain of idealism and theology.

Descartes' compromise in the form of the *dualism* of body and mind, may be regarded historically as a progressive step. The sacrifice of mind, the subject-matter of psychology, in order to further the independence of body and matter from domination by theological idealism, may have been a necessary phase of the struggle against reaction, but psychology today still suffers mortally from its effect. Dualism, three centuries later, remains the central problem. It was against this problem that Pavlov waged a fierce and uncompromising battle.

The modern struggle against the dualism of body and mind, however, was begun two hundred and fifty years before Pavlov.

Not long after Descartes' formulation of the dualism compromise, John Locke (1632-1704) took the first great step toward wrenching *mind* from the grip of scholastic idealism. The sweeping revolutionary movements of the seventeenth and eighteenth centuries could not afford to abide by the compromise. *Mind* could not be left as an exclusive domain of church doctrine, especially the doctrine of innate, God-given hierarchical ideas reflecting the hierarchy of feudal society. The onrushing revolutionary tide of capitalism and democracy required the theoretical annihilation of the doctrine of inborn feudal and scholastic ideas. Locke, in his *Essay on Human Understanding,* undertook the theoretical task. He held that there is no such thing as innate ideas of any kind, that simple ideas are based on the sense experience of individuals in the course of their lives, and that complex ideas are formed out of the simple sensory ones through *association*. *Sense experience* and *association* were viewed by Locke as the component elements of mind.

The revolutionary import of Locke's psychological theory was instantly grasped and his book at once became required reading for the intelligentsia of continental Europe as well as of England and the American colonies. The theory was taken over by the materialist encyclopedists, La Mettrie, Diderot, Helvetius and Holbach, and became an element in the ideology of the French Revolution. It exerted a profound influence on Jefferson, Franklin and Paine, among others, and became an element in the ideology of the American Revolution.

With the rise of the modern working classes and the revolutionary movement against capitalism, the legacy of Locke and particularly of Hobbes, Helvetius, Holbach and Diderot, together with Darwin's dynamic theory of evolution and the dialectical method of Hegel, was galvanized into the thorough and consistent monistic and scientific materialism of Marx and Engels.

Materialist philosophy was the first essential component in Pavlov's science of higher nervous activity, for its cardinal doctrine was the insistence that mind is a function of highly organized matter, the human brain.

A second component was the associationist psychology. Locke's psychological theory of sense experience and association constituted a devastating, literally a death-blow to the scholastic doctrine of mind and at the same time set in motion one of the four main currents of modern psychology—the sensory *association* theory of mental activity. This theory was expounded and developed by a multitude of philosophers and psychologists, among them: David Hume (1711-76), David Hartley (1705-57), James Mill (1773-1836), Herbert Spencer (1820-1903), and Alexander Bain (1818-1903) in England; Nicholai Tetens (1736-1807), Johannes Müller (1801-1858) and Wilhelm Wundt (1832-1920) in Germany; Sechenov in Russia; and James Rush and E. L. Thorndike in the United States.

The kernal of the theory of association lay in its contention that mental processes depend on simultaneity and succession in the connection of sensations, memory traces and ideas. Sensations or ideas become connected according to the way in which they appear before the mind, at the same time or one after the other.

The association theory of mental activity had become firmly established by the time Pavlov began his work. Almost all "schools" of psychology made use of it—and still do—including the introspective as well as the objective tendencies. Taken by itself, however, *association* leaves the dualism of body-mind in full sway. Whether or not the brain is recognized to be the organ of thought, as long as the functioning of the cerebral hemispheres is unknown, the theory of association remains a purely *mental* approach to mind. Almost all the associationists, including those mentioned above, attributed the work of association by simultaneity and succession to the brain—at first in the form of the motion of "animal spirits" and later as nervous conduction and even reflex activity. But there was as yet no *physiology* of the higher parts of the brain, and hence no knowledge of the nervous mechanisms of association. The theory of association remained for the most part a product of purely mental observation and self-observation until the work of Pavlov on the physiology of the cerebral hemispheres. Thus dualism remained entrenched in association psychology.

A more effective attack on dualism, however, was begun almost two hundred years before Pavlov, at first in speculative form but later through solid experimental work. This attack was mounted by the *physiological psychologists*. Physiological psychology, the second of the four main currents, has a history almost as extended as that of association psychology. In 1749 a book by David Hartley, *Observations on Man*, was published in London and created a considerable stir first on the continent in translation, and later in England. Hartley was an associationist and in his book he developed a theory of nervous activity underlying association phenomena. He was a materialist but not of the old reductionist type. He did not *reduce* mind to matter in motion but conceived of mental processes as a *function* of cerebral activity. He explained the process of *seeing*, for example, as vibrations in the ether setting in motion vibrations in the nerve tracts of the eye and leading to the brain. Once started, the vibrations in the brain continued first as after images and later as memory traces. The vibratory memory traces could be aroused again by means of association. When two sensory vibrations affect the nervous system at the same time or in succession, they become connected, according to Hartley, in such a way that whenever one is later reexcited the vibrations extend from it to the other and re-arouse it. Hartley also developed a theory of thought as being closely related to language in the form of word associations, the latter being likewise a matter of nerve-vibrations set in motion by the sounds of words. Word-sound vibrations, like non-verbal sensations, leave traces which can be re-aroused by association.

Here in Hartley's physiological treatment we have, as far as I have been able to ascertain, the first fully monist-materialist, as opposed to dualist-idealist, approach to mental processes. It avoids mechanistic materialism in psychology by the only possible means; mind or mental activity is viewed as a *function* of the material nervous activity of the brain. The brain is viewed as matter-in-motion while mind is viewed as a *quality*, a *property* or a *function* of this most highly organized material (nervous) motion.

Hartley's physiological psychology was greatly advanced for his period, but of course was purely theoretical, without any experimental support. Physiology in general and cerebral physiology in particular had not by 1749 made sufficient progress to allow the experimental development of physiological psychology.

Another hundred and fifty years of scientific progress were required before this could take place.

In the meantime, there were at least two more highly significant, but still purely theoretical, attempts to construct a thoroughly materialist physiological psychology; one by an American psychologist, James Rush (1786-1868) and the other by a Russian physiologist, I. M. Sechenov (1829-1905). Sechenov's *Reflexes of the Brain* was published in 1863, and Rush's *An Analysis of the Human Intellect* in 1865.[10] The latter was quite similar to Hartley's treatment, but was presented in much greater detail, incorporating many of the advances in science made in the intervening eighty-six years. Sechenov's work, however, was the most fruitful attempt to construct a physiological psychology, chiefly because it proposed for the first time that the reflex is the basic mechanism of higher, as of lower, cerebral activity. This suggestion, worked out theoretically by Sechenov, was taken up and experimentally verified and expanded by Pavlov some forty years later.

About the time Rush and Sechenov were developing their theoretically derived physiological approaches to psychology, three German physiologists were carrying on experimental investigations of the physiological-psychology of the sense organs and their cerebral connections; Johannes Müller, Ernest Heinrich Weber and the great universal scientist, Herman von Helmholtz. Their careful and concrete work on the physiological psychology of sensation and perception went a long way in preparing the ground for Pavlov's science of the functioning of the cerebral hemispheres.

The nineteenth century included also many scientists who together greatly advanced the study of physiology, especially the physiology of the nervous system and its apex, the brain. Among these were: Du Bois Raymond and Claude Bernard in France, Carl Ludwig and F. Vagus Goltz in Germany, and S. P. Botkin, I. F. Tsyon and of course I. M. Sechenov in Russia. This rapid advance of the physiology of the nervous system, penetrating as it did into at least the lower parts of the brain, was the indispensable condition for Pavlov's investigation of the cerebral hemispheres. More directly related to the latter was the work of two Viennese physiologists, Ewald Herring and Sigmund

Exner. Herring developed a theory of "Memory as a Function of Organized Matter[11] and Exner made a study of the localization of cerebral functions and developed a theory of the physiological basis of mental activity. A sign of the time immediately preceding the inception of Pavlov's work on the higher part of the brain was the founding in 1890 in Germany of the *Journal for the Psychology and Physiology of the Sense Organs*. The Journal included on its editorial board such men as Helmholtz, Exner and Herring.

These physiologists and physiological psychologists, together with a whole host of unknown and unsung co-workers in all the advanced nations, carried forward the assault on the Cartesian doctrine of the dualism of body and mind. But the assault could effect no more than relatively minor breaches in the idealist fortress of dualism so long as physiology and physiological psychology were stopped short of the *experimental* investigation of the higher nervous activity of the cerebral hemispheres.

The third main current in psychological thought, the experimental method, was initiated and primarily carried forward by the physiologists and physiological psychologists up to 1879. But in the latter year Wilhelm Wundt, previously discouraged by Helmholtz from becoming a physiologist because of his lack of knowledge of mathematics, opened at Leipzig, Germany, the first strictly psychological laboratory. He posited an association center located in the frontal lobes of the brain with nerve fibres running from all the sensory and motor areas of the cerebral cortex. On this *purely theoretical* physiological basis, Wundt designed and executed experiments concerned with the elucidation of *association* as the *physical* mechanism of mental processes. He was *not* a physiological psychologist since he did not view mind as a function of cerebral activity. Rather he developed a peculiarly psychological version of the dualism of mind and body called by him "psychophysical parallelism." With this doctrine he maintained that cerebral activity bore no causal or functional relationship to mental processes, but rather that the two were separate phenomena running as it were on parallel tracks. How these two unrelated but parallel tracks were coordinated, he never even conjectured. It would appear, however, that only a divine "pre-established harmony," on the order of Leibniz' or A. N. Whitehead's conception, could accomplish such a feat.

Be that as it may, Wundt's psychophysical parallelism became a popular if ill-concealed modern formula for maintaining the cardinal idealist doctrine of dualism. Still today the formula is at least *tacitly* employed by books and textbooks on psychology, which almost invariably begin with a sentence, a paragraph, or even a chapter or so on the anatomy and physiology of the nervous system and the brain, and then proceed for hundreds of pages to matters psychological without the slightest regard to the functioning of the organ of mental life. This bowing in the direction of, or lip service to, cerebral anatomy and physiology amounts to no more than a tacit avowal of Wundt's psychophysical parallelism and Descartes' dualism of body and mind, each with its own completely independent and unrelated laws of operation.[12]

Wundt's experimental approach to psychology, nevertheless, made important contributions to the theory of association and at the same time set in powerful motion the trend toward laboratory experimentation which today, throughout the world but particularly in the United States, is the dominant feature of academic psychology of whatever avowed theory or "school," introspective as well as objective. Experimentation is of itself, after all, no automatic guarantee of scientific authenticity or validity. Even the Society for Psychical Research carries on experimental investigation of such occult "phenomena" as extra-sensory perception, mediums, table-lifting and tapping, contact with the spirits of the departed, and the like. In experimentation validity depends on the subject to be investigated as well as on the authenticity of the method of investigating. In the case of Wundt, as of many of his followers including those in the United States, the experiments were and are important in so far as they discriminate and classify the phenomena of mental and behavioral association and disclose relationships among them.

The first great American and world exponent of the experimental approach to association phenomena in animal behavior was E. L. Thorndike, whose book, *Animal Intelligence,* started a movement one branch of which culminated in the "school" of *behaviorism*.[13] The main line of the movement begun by Thorndike still today, to a large extent, dominates experimental psychology in the United States—the investigation of association-behavior in animals as revealed in laboratory experiments involving primarily problem-solving situations.

The experimental method, the third of the four main currents in psychological thought, was enthusiastically embraced by Pavlov and incorporated and transformed in his coalescence of the physiology and psychology of the cerebral hemispheres.

The fourth and final current was initiated speculatively by George Herbert Spencer and given concrete validity by Charles Darwin. The evolutionary approach, applied to psychology by Spencer and Darwin and later generally accepted at least *formally* by all "schools," viewed the human mind and brain as the culmination of a long line of development from animal to man. Darwin himself traced one aspect of this process of anatomical-physiological-psychological evolution in his book on *The Expression of the Emotions in Man and Animals*. In the *Descent of Man* he demonstrated that the human brain had evolved from the animal brain and that many of the mental capacities of man must be traced to animal origins. The emphasis in Darwin's work on evolutionary psychology, as in all aspects of his work, was on *adaptation* to external conditions of life. The evolutionary approach with its stress on adaptation became a cornerstone on which Pavlov erected the science of higher nervous activity.

Pavlov's line of theoretical and scientific descent includes the four main currents in psychological thought—the associationist, the physiological, the experimental and the evolutionary—together with the monistic materialist philosophy of science. This heritage can be dramatized in the world-historic names of Wundt, Sechenov, Helmholtz, Darwin, Diderot and Marx.

Pavlov, according to the principles of monistic materialism, incorporated and transformed the four main currents into the science of higher nervous activity—the functioning of the cerebral hemispheres as the seat of mind and mental processes. Through concrete experimental work, with the indispensable aid of hundreds of co-workers, assistants and students, he demonstrated that the conditioned reflex constitutes the elementary physiological mechanism underlying all the unbelievably complex associative activity of animals and man in their never-ending phylogenetic and ontogenetic adaptation to environmental conditions of life. It was a grand synthesis of previously disparate psychological trends and directed toward the objective of finally solving, in its main outlines, the most difficult, the most obstructionist and at the same time the most vital theoretical problem facing mankind—the two-thousand-year-old body-mind problem with its pernicious doctrines of reductionism, dualism and psychophysical parallelism.

A comparison of the two theoretical lines of descent leads to two related conclusions.

First, with regard to the philosophy of science Freud's lineage lies outside the mainstream of scientific thought while Pavlov's lies squarely within it. More particularly this means that Freud worked within the unscientific if not anti-scientific, tradition, the chief features of which are idealism, subjectivism, metaphysics and irrationalism. Pavlov on the other hand, worked within the scientific tradition, the chief features of which are materialism, objectivism, evolution and rationality.

Second, with regard to the field of psychology itself, Freud worked outside the mainstream of psycholological thought. More particularly he built his system on such peripheral and discredited theories as: the interpretation of dreams; the translation of innate, stereotyped, archaic language symbols; anthropological myths; innate ideas and voluntarism. Pavlov on the other hand worked within the mainstream of psychological thought. More particularly he constructed the science of higher nervous activity on the solid foundation of established psychological, neurological, anatomical and physiological theories, facts and laws.

One might be tempted to conclude that Freud could succeed in building only a pseudo-scientific psychological system out of such a pseudo-scientific lineage. And conversely, that Pavlov could, on the basis of his lineage, succeed in developing a scientific approach to psychology. However, while there is certainly such an implication, it is by no means conclusive. Any conclusion must wait on an examination of the actual fruits of the two approaches.

Chapter VIII

FREUD'S APPROACH TO THE TWO MAIN PROBLEMS OF PSYCHOLOGY

Two KEY PROBLEMS in psychology are, on the one hand, the origin and development of mind in the human species and, on the other, the birth and growth of the individual mind. The former is closely associated with the fields of anthropology and human history, the latter with the fields of child development and education. The one is concerned with the transition from animal nature to human nature, the other with the development from infancy to adulthood.

Pavlov and Freud approached the two problems from opposite directions. Pavlov maintained that neither could be solved independently of the science of higher nervous activity, independently, that is, of knowledge of the structure and function of the brain and particularly of the cerebral hemispheres. Freud maintained that, in the absence of such a science, psychology must attempt the solution of the two problems in purely mental terms, without specific reference to the physical organ of psychic life.

Neither Freud nor Pavlov developed in detail their respective approaches to these key psychological problems. For the most part they proceeded on the basis of inferences, deductions and implications from their general and particular theories of higher activity, in each case posing questions for future investigation. Some of these questions were in fact later investigated by co-workers and followers.

We will now present the two approaches to the main problems of psychology so that we may evaluate their relative merit as rough draft programs for the further development of the science. The essential question to be answered, if possible, is: Which of these two approaches, that of Pavlov or that of Freud, forms the more *scientific* theoretical basis on which to construct the science of psychology? Each claims the prerogative. Which is the more valid claim? We proceed to an investigation of the two approaches so that we may be in a position to answer these questions.

As late as 1935 Freud maintained that psychology was not yet a science, that it lacked a common foundation, and that, apart from sensory physiology, there was no specialized knowledge in the field. Speaking of psychology, he wrote. "What does it comprise today, as taught in the schools? Apart from this valuable insight into sensoriphysiological matters, a number of classifications and definitions of our psychical processes which, thanks to common usage in speech, are now on the tongues of educated people. That is obviously inadequate for the comprehension of our psychical life. Have you not noticed that every philosopher, dramatist, novelist, historian or biographer arranges psychology for himself, adduces his own particular presuppositions as to the interconnections and aims of phychical activity, all more or less plausible and all equally precarious? There is clearly no common foundation. And so it comes about that on psychological ground, as it were, there is no authority and no observance; anyone may poach at will. If a question of physics or chemistry is raised, anyone without specialist knowledge will keep silent. But if an assertion about psychology is made, everyone feels entitled to express an opinion or to contradict. Seemingly, there is no specialist knowledge in this field." [1]

What psychology required, according to Freud—and according to Pavlov likewise—was a *common foundation* on which the science could be built. Freud was convinced that psychoanalysis, *the science of unconscious mental processes,* alone could furnish it.

Freud, himself, did not work out in detail the application of his "science of unconscious mental processes" to the field of psychology. He did, however, outline a solution to the two main problems of psychology, the origin and development of mind in the human species and in the individual human being.

From Primitive Mind to Civilized Mind

id, ego, super-ego

In his attempt to find a solution to the problem of the origin and development of mind in the human species, Freud proceeds on the basis of "The analogy between the process of cultural evolution and the path of individual development."[2] In drawing the analogy he selects those ethnological, anthropological and historical suppositions and theories which suit his purposes, and he depends heavily on myths and folklore. In particular he bases much of his thinking on the spectacular work of a completely discredited ethnologist-anthropologist, Robertson Smith.

Freud was aware of Smith's dubious status, but asserted his "good right to select" what would serve him best. Referring to his own book *Totem and Taboo,* Freud says, "I have often been vehemently reproached for not changing my opinions in later editions of my book, since more recent ethnologists have without exception discarded Robertson Smith's theories and have in part replaced them by others which differ extensively." Not only does he "still adhere" to Smith's theories, but he adds, "Above all, however, I am not an ethnologist, but a psychoanalyst. It was my good right to select from ethnological data what would serve me for my analytic work. The writing of the highly gifted Robertson Smith provided me with valuable points of contact with the psychological material of analysis and suggestions for the use of it. I cannot say the same of the work of his opponents."[3] Thus, at least in this field, Freud evaluates theories not in terms of their truth or falsity but with regard to their usefulness to psychoanalysis.

In many instances his method is to peg an hypothesis on a single historical fact and then to proceed independently of the facts and theories of history. "But we venture," he says, "to be independent of the historians in other respects and to blaze our own trail." The result is, as he himself says, "that in our hypothesis one assumption only rests on another."[4] Freud thus proposes to solve the first of the two great problems of psychology by means of analogy, expedient selection, independence of established material and arbitrary assumption.

Freud first gives "a glimpse of a hypothesis which may seem fantastic but which offers the advantage of establishing an unsuspected correlation between groups of phenomena that have hitherto been disconnected."[5] The fantastic is accomplished by bringing together, and giving "psychoanalytic translation" of, the totem, the totem meal and speculations on the earliest state of human society. With this combination Freud creates a myth which is repeated literally hundreds of times throughout his writings after 1912.

Prehistoric man, still half-animal, lived in a primal horde under the absolute and tyrannical domination of a violent and jealous father who kept all the women to himself and who drove away his sons as soon as they grew up.[6] This was a pre-gens, pre-tribal form of "society," without taboos or totems, in which the only principle of organization was the terrible power of the father. The human mind was at this juncture rudimentary, akin more to animal than to man. The conscious had not split away from The *Unconscious.* There was as yet no *conscience,* because there were no norms or values, and therefore no possibility of constructing an ideal. Instincts and emotions ruled supreme, unchallenged by any internal, mental, repressing agency.

Freud puts this mythical situation into a new terminology in which id, ego and super-ego replace, though (as we will see shortly) not precisely, the terms "unconscious," "conscious" and "conscience." In the new terminology, the mind of prehistoric man had not split into compartments—there was as yet no split between ego and id, nor was there a split in the ego between the ego proper and the super-ego. These evolved only with the further development of social organization.

In the primal horde, then, the human mind was, like that of the animal, one and undivided, in complete harmony with itself. All the conflict was external, between the members of the "horde." Somehow, according to Freud, this external conflict finally reached a crucial point and "one day the brothers who had been driven out came together, killed and devoured their father and so made an end of the patriarchal horde. . . . Cannibal savages as they were, it goes without saying that they devoured their victim as well as killing him." From this pre-historic deed "A sense of guilt made its appearance."[7] and this was the beginning of the strictly human mind with its splits between id, ego and super-ego. The sense of guilt formed the first dividing walls in the form of censorship between id and ego and ego and super-ego, and made *repression* the great dynamic force in mental processes.

This is Freud's myth of the *origin* of the human mind. The *evolution* of mind, according to him, took place in two stages, the tribal stage and civilization. The tribal stage of mental evolution was characterized by the progressively more extensive *renunciation of instinctual drives and impulses*. We have seen how Freud visualized the first instinctual renunciations as a result of the original sin. Taboos on incest and on killing the totem animal extended the domination of repression. Each step of man's history was initiated and made possible by an act of instinctual renunciation. The pre-condition for material progress was, according to Freud, the original repression of an instinct. In most cases the instinct to be renounced was a component of the sexual instincts. He gives many examples of such instinct renunciation but perhaps the most striking one is his psychoanalytic translation of the Prometheus myth. It is Freud's version of how man gained control over fire. He arrives at his version by means of the psychoanalytical interpretation of the myth in which the imagery is treated as symbolic and the stereotyped meaning is translated as in the interpretation of dreams.

He first assumes on the basis of his general theory that "the acquisition of fire necessitated a renunciation of instinct," and then by means of symbol reading he reconstructs the great event: "It is as if primitive man had had the impulse, when he came in contact with fire, to gratify an infantile pleasure in respect of it and put it out with a stream of urine. The legends that we possess leave no doubt that flames shooting upwards like tongues were originally felt to have a phallic sense. Putting out fire by urinating therefore represented a sexual act with a man, an enjoyment of masculine potency in homosexual rivalry. Whoever was the first to deny himself this pleasure and spare the fire was able to take it with him and break it in to his own service. By curbing the fire of his own sexual passion he was able to tame fire as a force of nature. This great cultural victory was thus a reward for refraining from the gratification of an instinct. Further it is as if man had placed woman by the hearth as the guardian of the fire he had taken captive, because her anatomy makes it impossible for her to yield to such a temptation." [8]

Freud interprets the punishment of Prometheus, chained to a rock to be eaten bit by bit by vultures, as the revengeful wrath of the id at being further repressed. Prometheus' "crime" was that "he had renounced his instinctual desires and had shown how beneficent and at the same time how essential was such renunciation for the purposes of civilization." [9]

The tribal period of human pre-history consists, according to Freud, in the formation of thousands of such instinctual renunciations or repressions stretching over a period of tens of thousands of years. Each instance of repression initiates a step, whether small or great, in the direction of the civilized period of human history. In this process there is, Freud holds, a double effect on the mental apparatus. On the one hand, with each successive instinctual renunciation the unconscious, instinct-laden id is further filled with repressed impulses. Thus it becomes a writhing pit of rebellious innate and repressed drives all highly charged with psychic energy and insistently and irrepressibly demanding discharge. The more progress society makes, that is, the more instincts that are renounced and suppressed, the more the id is packed with repressions retaining their cathexes. Thus, as Freud puts it, the id becomes "a chaos, a cauldron of seething excitement." It is filled with instincts and their repressions, and "these instincts fill it with energy, but it has no organization and no unified will, only an impulsion to obtain satisfaction for the instinctual needs, in accordance with the pleasure principle. The laws of logic—above all the law of contradiction—do not hold for processes in the id. Contradictory impulses exist side by side without neutralizing each other or drawing apart. . . . In the id there is nothing corresponding to the idea of time, no recognition of the passage of time and no alteration of mental processes by the passage of time . . . impressions which have been pushed down into the id are virtually immortal. . . . Naturally, the id knows no values, no good and evil, no mortality. . . . Instinctual cathexes seeking discharge, that, in our view, is all that the id contains." [10]

Thus while the progress of tribal society depends on renunciation and suppression of the instincts of the id, the latter is at the same time itself supercharged with new repressed and highly cathected material. Society demands that the lid be pressed down tight on the kettle of instincts which is the id, but this merely acts to build up steam-pressure. This is one side of the double effect of social progress on the mental apparatus.

The other side is the formation of a part of the id into an ego representing the accumulated experience of the external world. The ego separates off from the id in the course of dvelopment of tribal society. While the id represents the untamed passions, the ego represents intelligence and reason. While the id operates solely on the basis of instinct satisfaction according to the pleasure principle, the ego operates on the basis of knowledge according to the reality principle. The ego originates in the experiences of the perceptual system and is designed to represent the demands of the external world.

The ego, however, is weak, according to Freud, "it borrows its energy from the id. . . . On the whole the ego has to carry out the intentions of the id." And he goes on to give an analogy, "One might compare the relation of the ego to the id with that between a rider and his horse. The horse provides the locomotive energy, and the rider has the prerogative of determining the goal and of guiding the movements of his powerful mount towards it. But all too often in the relations between the ego and the id we find a picture of the less ideal situation in which the rider is obliged to guide his horse in the direction in which it itself wants to go."[11] The ego is hard-pressed to keep the instincts under control and the repressed material repressed. It must successfully perform both these functions in order to meet the exigencies of the external world, natural and social. If it fails, the id will lead the ego to certain destruction at the hands of tribal society (for transgressing taboos) or at the hands of nature (for ignoring objective circumstances). Thus the ego as formed in the course of tribal society is forced, according to Freud, to carry on a two-front battle against the id and against the external world. But even this is not all.

The ego itself is split into ego proper and super-ego or conscience. The super-ego, originating in remorse and guilt for the deed of patricide, develops along with the renunciation of instincts, and, indeed, is itself the repressing agency. At first it is the result of repression and then it becomes a tyrant demanding ever more repression. Thus the super-ego, as the agent of instinctual renunciation, in effect, becomes, according to Freud, the motive force of social and mental development. It is the repository of taboos, and later of morality, ethical values and standards and religious commandments. The super-ego incites the ego into battle against the id.

The ego is caught between three forces: the id, the super-ego and the external world. "The proverb tells us," Freud says, "that one cannot serve two masters at once. The poor ego has a still harder time of it; it has to serve three harsh masters, and has to do its best to reconcile the claims and demands of all three. These demands are always divergent and often seem quite incompatible; no wonder the ego so frequently gives way under its task. The three tyrants are the external world, the super-ego and the id. . . . In this way, goaded on by the id, hemmed in by the super-ego, and rebuffed by reality, the ego struggles to cope with its economic task of reducing the forces and influences which work in it and upon it to some kind of harmony."[12]

Freud paints a grim picture of the tribal mind. From the simple, if chaotic, unity of the primal-horde, rudimentary mind, the progressively more stringent instinctual renunciation of tribal society brought about a three-way split in the mental apparatus. Each component—id, ego, and super-ego—are set against one another in essentially irreconcilable antagonism. Grim as is this view of the tribal mind, however, it is mild in comparison with Freud's conception of the mind of civilized man.

Two mental developments, according to Freud, gave rise to the civilized mind and hence to civilized society: *the return of the repressed* and *sublimation*.

By *the return of the repressed* Freud signifies his notion, mentioned earlier, of the *archaic heritage*. In the tens of thousands of years of evolution of the tribal mind, certain *mental formations* had become hereditary. Biologically inherited mental traits, memories, impulses and ideas are, according to Freud, deposited in the human unconscious. They are inborn in the unconscious super-ego as well as the unconscious id. For example, the instinctive impulse to have incestuous sexual relations is innate in the id, while the tribal taboo-prohibition on incest is innate in the super-ego. Another example would be the unconscious impulse to urinate on fire inborn in the id and the taboo-prohibition against the act inborn in the super-ego. Civilized mind is marked off from primitive tribal mind in part by the innate features of the archaic heritage, the phylogenetic return of the repressed.

This mental inheritance, thousands of years old, is always, according to Freud, *ambivalent,* that is, the deposit in the id drives toward satisfaction and the deposit in the super-ego countermands the order. The civilized mind loves and hates at the same time. Based for instance, in part on the innate (id) impulse of the archaic heritage relating to hatred of the patriarchal father culminating in patricide, the modern son hates his father; but based ambivalently also on the innate (super-ego) sense of guilt and remorse for this original sin, the modern son also loves his father. Again, based on the hereditary pre-historic incest instinct the modern son has unconscious (id) impulses to have sex relations with his mother; but based on the innate taboo (super-ego) prohibition on incest, the modern son is repelled by such incestuous impulses. Thus the roots of the Oedipus complex are inborn mental deposits.

"The man of prehistoric ages," Freud says, "survives unchanged in our Unconscious." [13] He holds that "the archaic heritage of mankind includes not only dispositions, but also ideational contents, memory-traces of the experiences of former generations." And if there is any remaining doubt about his meaning, he adds: "On second thought I must admit that I have argued as if there were no question that there exists an inheritance of memory-traces of what our forefathers experienced, quite independently of direct communication and of the influence of education by example. When I speak of an old tradition still alive in a people, of the formation of a national character, it is such an inherited tradition, and not one carried by word of mouth, that I have in mind. . . . This state of affairs is made more difficult, it is true, by the present attitude of biological science, which rejects the idea of acquired qualities being transmitted to descendents. . . . If we accept the continued existence of such memory traces in our archaic inheritance, then we have bridged the gap between individual and mass psychology and can treat peoples as we do the individual neurotic. Though we may admit that for the memory-traces in our archaic inheritance we have so far no stronger proof than those remnants of memory evoked by analytic work, which call for a derivation from phylogenesis, yet this proof seems to me convincing enough to postulate such a state of affairs." And he adds the statement so often utilized with regard to his assumptions, namely that without such an assumption psychoanalysis can make no further progress: "If things are different, then we are unable to advance one step further on our way, either in psychoanalysis or in mass psychology." The concept of an innate mental heritage from tribal society is an absolutely essential feature of Freud's psychoanalysis and depth psychology. "It is," he says, "bold, but inevitable." Without it, stereotyped symbolism and symbol translation are impotent to perform their assigned function as revealers of the otherwise inaccessible Unconscious mental processes.

The idea-memory of the terrible deed of original sin that started mind and society on its evolutionary course is, according to Freud, an hereditary mental deposit in the human unconscious. Men unconsciously know that they had a primeval father and killed him. "After these considerations" (affirming the reality of the archaic mental heritage), he says, "I have no qualms in saying that men have always known—in this particular way — that once upon a time they had a primeval father and killed him." [14]

This question of the return of the repressed in the form of a biologically inborn mental heritage from primitive man is truly a crucial one for Freud. Simple animal or human instincts alone are far too restricted in character to meet the requirements of his science of The Unconscious. If he had not insisted on the concept of an innate archaic heritage, his main claim to novelty, the "discovery" of the *underworld* of The Unconscious, would have been impossible. At best the Oedipus complex, the infantile stages of sexuality, and all the rest would have been acquired character traits of particular concrete people of a particular class living in a particular place at a particular time. There could have been no claim of universality. But with the assumption of a mental heritage from far off times, he can, on his own grounds, claim universality for his "discoveries." It alone makes it possible for him to lay claim to the establishment of an entirely new science, the science of unconscious mental processes.

The civilized mind, according to Freud, not only has to renounce, suppress and maintain the repression of the inborn instincts of the id, but it has to repress also all the innate deposits of the archaic heritage from primitive tribal man. The latter's task was hard enough. The task of the civilized mind is many times more difficult. It has to deal with the return of the repressed as well as with initial instinctual renunciation.

In addition to this greatly increased difficulty, civilized mind, according to Freud, has another disadvantage compared with tribal mind. The tribal mind was not as rigidly restricted with regard to the satisfaction of sexual instincts, drives, impulses and emotions. There was no institution of monogamy and therefore the psychic energy of the taboo-prohibited instincts could be transferred to the full satisfaction of the unfettered heterosexual, non-incestual, sexual instincts. Freud maintained that the psychic energy of the sexual instincts, called libido, was more fluid than others and that it could displace its aim without materially losing its intensity.[15] Primitive man had little need for the transfer of sexual psychic energy or libido to non-sexual activity, because of his greater latitude of strictly sexual activity.

With the rise of monogomy, under the goading of the super-ego, the situation, Freud maintained, changed radically. The civilized mind could not in most cases find adequate sexual outlets and therefore was forced to sublimate this energy. *Sublimation* is the transfer of libido to non-sexual activity as an outlet for frustrated sexual psychic energy. Thus culture and civilization, modern society, are the outcome of this process of sublimation peculiar to civilized mind. "Sublimation of instinct," Freud says, "is an especially conspicuous feature of cultural evolution; this it is that makes it possible for the higher mental operations, scientific, artistic, ideological activities, to play such an important part in civilized life."[16]

Once started on this road to civilization and culture, the human mind simply created greater and greater difficulties for itself. Every step in progress required further instinctual renunciation and suppression of the archaic heritage; more restriction of instinct gratification, especially of a sexual nature; and also more libido to be sublimated. With such continued "progress," it becomes more and more difficult to effect sufficient transfer of instinctual energy to socially acceptable ends. After a certain point is reached civilized mankind becomes chronically and universally neurotic as a result both of insufficient sexual gratification and of inadequate sublimation. Thus civilization and culture are viewed by Freud as leading inevitably to frustration, unhappiness and neurosis, in spite of the great accomplishment of modern times—or rather precisely because of the great progress, material and cultural, that has been made.

The repressed libido which cannot find discharge directly or through sublimation will eventually in most cases find outlet in tension, anxiety and neurotic symptoms. Freud concludes that in civilized society "we are all ill, i.e., neurotic"[17] and he conjectures on the possibility "that many systems of civilization—or epochs of it—possibly even the whole of humanity—have become neurotic under the pressure of the civilizing trends." And he speaks of "the diagnosis of collective neuroses" and "the pathology of civilized communities." [18]

The sexual instincts and the sexual archaic heritage with their libido form of psychic energy comprise the main but not the sole content of the repressed unconscious. The death instincts, including particularly the instincts of aggression, cruelty and destruction, also, according to Freud, undergo repression in the course of social evolution. The outcome of the repression of these instincts, however, is not mass neurosis; it is mass destruction in war. The death, destructive and aggressive instincts have been the ultimate cause of wars and inquisitions throughout the history of civilization.

Of primitive man, whose mental traits are still part of our unconscious, Freud says: "He was, in truth, a very violent being, more cruel and more malign than other animals. He liked to kill, and killed as a matter of course." At any time, given the relaxation of social restraints on the aggressive instincts, for example, during states of war, civilized man, according to Freud, reverts to the primitive. "The earlier mental state may not have manifested itself for years, but none the less it is so far present that it may at any time again become the mode of expression of the forces in the mind, and that exclusively, as though all later developments had been annulled, undone. . . . The primitive stages can always be reestablished." Freud concludes, "And so, if we are to be judged by the wishes in our Unconscious, we are, like primitive man, simply a gang of murderers."

In 1915 Freud wrote of World War I, then in progress, "From the foregoing observations we may already derive this consolation—that our mortification and our grievous disillusionment regarding the uncivilized behavior of our world-compatriots in this war are shown to be unjustified. They were based on an illusion to which we had abandoned ourselves. In reality our fellow-citizens have not sunk so low as we feared, because they had never risen so high as we believed. That the greater units of humanity, the peoples and states, have mutually abrogated their moral restraints naturally prompted these individuals to permit themselves relief for a while from the heavy pressure of civilization and to grant a passing satisfaction to the instincts it holds in check." War is, according to Freud, the inevitable periodic revolt of the death and aggressive instincts against their restraint by society and the individual super-ego.

Civilization and culture are, according to Freud, "built up on renunciation of instinctual gratification," particularly of the two general classes of instincts, sex or Eros and death or aggression. The repression of the latter terminates in the return of the repressed in the form of war; and the repression of the former ends in the return of the repressed in the form of neurotic symptoms.

The outlook presented by psychoanalysis is indeed bleak. Its originator become more and more pessimitsic and cynical. He was convinced by his own trend of thought that "the price of progress in civilization is paid in forfeiting happiness." [20] The outcome of his social psychology made him wonder whether civilization was after all worth the effort.

Such is Freud's solution of the problem of the origin of the human mind and its development from the primitive to civilized state. It is the story of the phylogenetic repression of instincts and the revenge they eventually take.

We turn now to an examination of the various forms assumed by this revenge in the development of the civilized mind from infancy to adulthood—Freud's solution of the second great problem of psychology.

From Infant Mind to Adult Mind

Freud worked out his solution of the problem of the ontogenetic development of the human mind as a by-product of analysis of his patients. The fact that this meant proceeding by analogy of the sick with the healthy did not perturb Freud in the least, because, as we saw in his views on the phylogenetic evolution of mind, he held that there is no real line of demarcation between mental health and mental illness—we are all neurotic. The difference, if any, is one of degree and not of kind.

Through interpretation, by means of symbol translation, of the subjective content of his patients' neurotic symptoms—their fantasies and fixations, delusions and dreams—he came to certain conclusions about the phases of development of the individual mind. These phases, he maintains, roughly parallel the phases of mental evolution from primal-horde to civilized mind.

To begin with, the mind of the infant is similar to that of pre-historic man prior to the primordial deed of patricide. The infant at birth possesses no (active) super-ego and his ego is limited, as in pre-historic man, to sense experience of the external world. Only his id is in operation, and is subject to no internal repressive processes. Thus there is as yet no split between id and ego and none between ego proper and super-ego. His mind forms one harmonious whole.

There is, however, a big difference between the infant mind and the pre-historic mind. While the latter, to reach the level of civilized mind, had to undergo thousands of years of experience which only gradually became hereditary in the form of the archaic heritage, the infant mind at birth, is, according to Freud, endowed with an innate constitution including all the essential phases of phylogenetic evolution. This constitution is more or less the same in all, and only takes on its individual character under the vicissitudes of life. The seat of this inborn mental constitution is The Unconscious, including the id and the unconscious elements of the ego and the super-ego. It includes the instincts, under the general headings of Eros and death, their repressions, and the return of the repressed, the archaic mental heritage of race memories, taboos, and the innate perverted forms of instinctual discharge resorted to under the duress of repression. The latter include: First, the phases of infantile sexuality, which, according to Freud, are hereditary aberrations through which all children must pass; second, the Oedipus formations which are different in boys and in girls; third, the phenomena of the castration complex and penis envy; and fourth, the tendencies toward sadism and masochism. These are hereditary phases which all "normal," "healthy" children must undergo in the process of developing from infant to adult mind in civilized society. They only remain dormant until growth and conditions of life call them into operation.

Infantile Sexuality

Freud places primary emphasis on the early years of childhood, because it is during this time, he maintains, that the individual repeats the entire course of phylogenetic development. "Each individual," he says, "repeats in some abbreviated fashion during childhood the whole course of the development of the human race."[21] Now we have already seen that in Freud's view the development of the human race is the story of the successive repression of animal-pre-historic and primitive-human instincts and mental traits of the archaic heritage. Thus we will not be surprised that Freud, by means of translation of the symbolic language of dreams, myths and fantasies (itself "a mode of expression which has never been individually acquired" and which is "to be regarded as a racial heritage") "finds" that the first phase of the childhood mind is *cannibalistic*. The cannibalistic phase of the infantile mind is a pre-genital sexual manifestation centering around the erogenous zone of the mouth and is manifested in sucking and eating—the sexual aim of which is "the *incorporation* of the object into one's own body." Freud calls this "the *oral*, or if one will, the cannibalistic" phase. It is characterized by the instinctive, archaic impulse to *eat* things. The second pre-genital phase is called "the *sadistic-anal* organization." It is characterized by the impulse to "mastery," particularly to master the bowels, and involves "the erogenous mucous membranes of the bowel"[22] This phase is an hereditary infantile form of the long repressed aggressive cruelty and violence instincts of pre-historic man.

The connection which Freud makes between the pre-historic instincts and the particular erogenous zones indicates that sexual perversion in which these zones played a dominant part had according to him become substitute gratifications for the prohibited aggressive instincts. In the infant, both the original instincts (cannibalism, aggression or sadism) and the substitute formations (the sexual perversions) are considered to be part of the archaic heritage of the mind of modern man. The infant must successfully repress or sublimate both the instincts *and* the perverted forms of expression sought as a result of their original repression. If the child does not fully succeed in repressing or sublimating these phases, he may either be *fixated* in one or another of them or in later life he may *regress* to them.

Here already we see the importance to Freud's system of the notion of an innate mental archaic heritage. For it alone furnishes a rationale for the supposed combination in childhood of primitive instincts and the return of the repressed in the form of inborn sexual aberrations and perversions. This is decisive for Freud since he pins much of the future character, normalcy and mental health of the individual on the way in which the infantile pre-genital phases are repressed or sublimated.

The crucial period, then, is the first four years of life. After the age of four, according to Freud, the sex-life of children passes through a latency period lasting until puberty. From puberty to adolescence the child in the normal course of events passes from the phallic to the genital phase. But the pre-genital phases in the first four years determine to a large extent the entire course of the individual's life. Let us see how Freud derives traits of character from the pre-genital phases. We take as an example the relation between the anal sadistic phase and the formation of a particular type of character.[23]

The type of character in question exhibits a regular combination of three peculiarities; orderliness, parsimony and obstinacy, or, as Freud put it elsewhere, pedantry, avarice and stubborness.[24] He maintains that a character notable for obstinacy, orderliness and avarice is derived from a childhood in which the sadistic-anal phase had endured longer than ordinary, long enough, in fact, for the child to be classed as an "anal erotic." The character traits are then accounted for in terms of sublimation of the infantile sexual perversion of anal eroticism.

Freud traces the character trait of *obstinacy* to the "observation" that the anal-erotic child takes a long time to empty his bowels and to learn to control them. "As infants," Freud says, "they seem to have been among those who refuse to empty the bowel when placed on the chamber, because they derive an incidental pleasure from the act of defacation. . . . From these indications we infer that the erotogenic significance of the anal zone is intensified in the innate sexual constitution of these persons." This obstinacy and stubborness in emptying the bowels, due to sexual pleasure, sooner or later is sublimated, that is, its sexual aim is given up and the libidinal energy is transferred wholly or in part to stubborness and obstinacy in general. Thus does anal eroticism, itself a prolongation of the sadistic-anal phase, give rise to a permanent character trait formed within the first four years of a child's life. The sublimation takes place by two means: First, because of hereditary patterns derived from racial evolution; and second because of pressure from society in the form of "toilet training."

Freud attempts to establish a connection between *orderliness* and the anal-sadistic phase temporarily fixated in anal eroticism by means of "a reaction formation against things that are unclean and intrusive and ought not to be on the body." Sublimated, this becomes general orderliness in petty matters.

He attempts, finally, to connect anal eroticism with parsimony, avarice or interest in money by means of symbolism supposedly employed in dreams, myths and fairy tales. "In reality," he says, "wherever archaic modes of thought predominate or have persisted—in ancient civilizations, in myths, fairy-tale and superstition, in unconscious thoughts and dreams, and in the neuroses—money comes into the closest relation with excrement." The anal and erotic child, Freud maintains, hordes his faeces, is ungenerous with it, will not give it to his mother or nurse. When the sublimation is achieved, the interest in money is arising about the same time and so facilitates the transfer of sexual aim from faeces to money. "The original anal-erotic interest in defaecation," Freud says, "is, as you know, destined to be extinguished in later years; it is in these years that the interest in money is making its appearance as something new which was unknown in infancy. This makes it easier for the impulse, which is in process of relinquishing its aim, to be carried over to the new one." The external circumstance of growing contact with money makes it *easier* to make the connection between faeces and money, but Freud's main point is that this connection is innate as part of the archaic heritage from primitive times. Money and faeces are connected, he maintained, in the racial unconscious, as revealed in the translation of symbols found in dreams and myths. Contact with money serves only to awaken the inborn unconscious archaic connection between the two.

The temporary fixation of the anal-sadistic phase constitutes the infantile sexual perversion called anal-eroticism which in turn leads through sublimation to the grouping of three permanent traits of character. The character type exhibiting obstinacy, orderliness and avarice, Freud therefore calls "the anal character." As a program for future psychoanalytic investigation he says, "One ought to consider whether other types of character do not also show a connection with the excitability of particular erotogenic zones." One could then speak of oral, eurethral, phallic and genital character types. Such investigations have in fact been carried out by Freud's followers.

The Oedipus Complex

So far we have been examining Freud's theory of the *phasic development* of the infantile and child mind in relation to certain erogenous zones and the instincts and archaic heritages connected with them. The *Oedipus complex,* on the other hand, concerns *the finding of sexual objects* during the various phases of development.

The Oedipus complex is, according to Freud, "a phenomenon determined and laid down for him (the child) by heredity." The vicissitudes of individual life determine the particular form the complex takes, but the general features are innate and therefore the same in all instances. The Oedipus complex is, for Freud, the most important and decisive inborn legacy from primal horde and primitive tribal times. Its component elements are, on the one hand, the primal horde instinct involving incestuous sexual relations and on the other the inborn archaic heritage involving the taboo-ban both on incest and on killing the totem animal, symbol of the father.[25]

In Freud's view, literally everything depends on the way in which the Oedipus complex is worked out. Thus the outcome is decisive both for the individual and ultimately for society.

What then is Freud's conception of the fateful Oedipus* complex?

The rudimentary or anaclitic stage of the Oedipus complex takes place, according to Freud, in the infantile cannibalistic-oral phase of development. It consists in taking the mother's (or wet-nurse's) breast as the sexual object. The fact that the breast serves nutritional as well as libidinal needs signifies, Freud maintains, that the erotic component at first depends on the feeding instinct. Soon, however, the infant begins to suck for the pleasure of sucking, and may substitute his thumb for the nipple. In this way the child breaks away from the initial form of the Oedipus complex and substitutes for his mother's breast an element of his own body as a sexual object. This step marks the transition to infantile auto-eroticism. Further development involves the renunciation of auto-eroticism and the finding once again of an external sexual object in the form of a person.

*Freud tells "the shocking and terrible story of the myth": "You all know the Greek myth of King Oedipus, whose destiny it was to slay his father and to wed his mother, who did all in his power to avoid the fate prophesied by the oracle, and who in self-punishment blinded himself when he discovered that in ignorance he had committed both these crimes." (Freud, *Introductory Lectures on Psychoanalysis,* p. 278.)

Up to this point, probably around the age of two, the pattern of development of boys and girls is identical. But from the moment a sexual object in the form of a person is found, the two take separate paths. The little boy develops a "straightforward sexual object cathexis towards his mother"[26] and the little girl towards her father. From this point on, we have to trace Freud's conception of the inner workings of the Oedipus complex separately in boys and girls, the outcome of which, he maintained, determined the widely different masculine and feminine character and intellectual capacity.

"The task before each new human being," Freud says, "is to master the Oedipus complex."[27] The future man and woman depends on how the child accomplishes this task. But the way in which he or she does so is primarily laid down by heredity, both by the different innate features of the two sexes, and by the inborn constitutional peculiarities of the individual. We begin as Freud did with the working out of the Oedipus complex in boys.

About the time the boy finds a sexual object in his mother, the mental operation of repression of his sexual instincts has already set in. Knowledge of his sexual aims is thus withdrawn from him, and his sexual attraction to his mother appears to him as simple love. His mother is his *love-object*. About the same time, too, the innate archaic incest barrier, aided and abetted by the prohibitions of contemporary society, is coming into operation. This further acts to conceal the sexual nature of his feelings for his mother.

Again about this same time—it is a crucial period in the boy's life—he develops, according to Freud, an *ambivalent* attitude toward his father. On the one hand, the son identifies himself with his father, admires him and wants to be "just like him" when he grows up. He takes his father for his ideal. On the other hand, the son notices that the father stands in his way with his mother and he begins to regard him as a disturbing rival. These feelings develop into the desire to get rid of his father and to take his place. The identification with the father now has the ambivalent content of admiration and respect on one side and the death-wish on the other. This too is the innate unfolding, tens of thousands of years later, of the primal-horde sons' attitude toward their father, their wish to be like him and their wish to kill him.

The boy's primitively preordained, inborn fate is working him into a highly dramatic situation; the son loves his mother while he respects, idealizes and hates his father, and wishes him dead. There is here certainly sufficient emotional and tensional dynamite to blow apart an adult mind, not to mention the mind of a two, three, or four year old child. The child, however, does not have to resolve the terrible conflicts intellectually and without help. "The Oedipus complex," Freud says, "must come to an end because the time has come for its dissolution, just as the milk-teeth fall out when the permanent ones begin to press forward. Although the majority of human children individually pass through the Oedipus complex, yet after all it is a phenomenon determined and laid down for him by heredity, and must decline according to schedule when the next preordained stage of development arrives." [28] The main impulsion toward termination comes from a combination of internal sources—the masturbation instinct, a component of the sexual instincts; the innate archaic heritage of the *sense of guilt* stemming from the original sin of patricide; and the *fear of castration* stemming from the innate archaic memory of the punishment for incest meted out by the father of the primal-horde to his sons.

The death-wish against the father and the incest-wish with regard to the mother together operate to call into action the inborn sense of guilt in relation to incest and father-murder. At the same time, under the stimulation of the sexual love of his mother, the boy begins to be narcissistically interested in his own genitals and to masturbate. The innate sense of guilt connected with incest and patricide are transferred to the act of infantile masturbation. The punishment for incest is, according to the innate archaic heritage, castration. Thus the sense of guilt and fear of punishment by castration are transferred from incest and patricide and concentrated on masturbation.

This unfolding innate structure is helped along, Freud maintains, by an external but inevitable chain of events. The mother or nurse threatens the boy with castration, usually telling him that his father will carry out the threat. The boy at first, though fearing the punishment, does not fully believe in it. There then takes place a momentous and decisive event in the boy's life. "The observation that finally breaks down the child's unbelief," Freud says, "is the sight of the female genitalia. Some day or other it happens that the child whose own penis is such a proud possession obtains a sight of the genital parts of a little girl; he must then become convinced of the absence of a penis in a creature so like himself. With this, however, the loss of his own penis becomes imaginable, and the threat of castration achieves its delayed effect."

The boy (four years old), convinced of the genuineness of the castration threat, is faced with a major decision: Either he must give up his narcissistic infantile masturbation and its closely related sexual love-interest in his mother or he will lose his penis. "Normally, in this conflict the first of these forces triumphs; the child's ego turns away from the Oedipus complex." Thus according to Freud "the boy's Oedipus complex succumbs to the dread of castration."

The process of turning away from the Oedipus complex has momentous consequences. For in the course of it, the boy's super-ego is formed and his mind becomes "civilized," that is, it is now complete, with an id, ego and super-ego. The super-ego is formed out of fear of castration and out of remorse for the incest-wish and death-wish. In this process the authority of the father forms the kernal of the super-ego. The latter takes its severity from the father, perpetuates his prohibition against incest, and so insures the ego as far as possible against a recurrence of the incest-wish. The libidinal energy of the Oedipus complex in the boy, released by the destruction of the complex, is transferred to desexualized aims in the form of sublimations, particularly socially acceptable ones of schoolwork and play — later to be transferred to work, creative activity, science, the arts, etc.

This, according to Freud, is the "normal" or "ideal" solution of the Oedipus complex in boys. It establishes the "masculine character" with its strength of will, its discipline, its rational, logical features, its interest in the outside world and in civilization and culture. But this ideal resolution in which the Oedipus complex is utterly destroyed by the fear of castration is seldom if ever achieved. The more common outcome is the repression rather than the destruction of the complex. In this more *usual* case, the repression of the incest and death wishes, and of the fears and guilt feelings, leads to reversions and regressions, to perversions and aberrations, to delinquency and crime, and in general to neuroses. "It is not a great step," Freud says, "to assume that here we have come upon the borderland between normal and pathological which is never very sharply defined. If the ego has really not achieved much more than a repression of the complex, then this latter persists unconsciously in the *id*, and will express itself later on in some pathogenic effect." [29]

The destruction or repression of the Oedipus complex, Freud maintains, preserves the boy's penis but temporarily at least also represses his sexual activity, and a period of latency sets in lasting until puberty—that is from the age of four or five until around twelve or thirteen. At that time there is a resurgence of the complex, the intensity, type and duration of which depends largely on the way in which the infantile Oedipus phase had been worked out. The task of the young man then becomes one of breaking away from the parents so that he may find a mate and take his place in the community. "From the time of puberty onward," Freud says, "the human individual must devote himself to the great *task of freeing himself from the parents*." [30]

For Freud, Oedipus makes—or breaks—the man, and civilization, too, for that matter. How does he account for the development of the grown woman from the infant girl?

Whereas in boys the castration complex *terminates* the Oedipus complex, in girls, on the contrary, the castration complex according to Freud *initiates* the Oedipus complex. Freud speaks of "a momentous discovery which little girls (age two, three or four) are destined to make," and continues, "They notice the penis of a brother or playmate, strikingly visible and of large proportions, at once recognize it as the superior counterpart of their own small and inconspicuous organ, and from that time forward fall a victim to envy for the penis. . . . She has seen it and knows that she is without it and wants to have it." This initiates what Freud calls "the masculinity complex of women" involving "the hope of some day obtaining a penis in spite of everything and so of becoming like a man."

Little boys, when they see the bodies of little girls, develop, according to Freud, one of two attitudes toward them: "horror of the mutilated creature or triumphant contempt for her." In either case, they develop a strong sense of male superiority. Together these developments "permanently determine the boy's relations to women." Thus the ideology of male superiority, Freud holds, is fated by biological and archaic heredity. In addition, the other side of this superiority is likewise fated. "After a woman has become aware of the wound to her narcissism, she develops, like a scar, a sense of inferiority. When she has passed beyond her first attempt at explaining her lack of a penis as being a punishment personal to herself and has realized that that sexual character is a universal one, she begins to share the contempt felt by men for a sex which is the lesser in so important a respect." A boy is *destined* to feel superior and a girl inferior and these feelings determine permanent attitudes in the grown man and woman.

This, however, is still only the subjective aspect of the sense of male superiority and female inferiority. Freud gives this feeling objective validity by maintaining that men are fated by the innate Oedipus complex to be in fact superior, while women are fated by the same complex to be in fact inferior. In boys and men, as we have seen, Freud maintains that a strong super-ego is the heir of the Oedipus complex, by the agency of the castration complex. In girls and women, on the other hand, he maintains that fated somehow in the course of the girl's childhood is a transformation from penis envy to an equation of "penis = child." She gives up her wish for a penis and puts in place of it a wish for a child; and *with this purpose in view* she takes her father as a love-object. Her mother becomes the object of her jealousy." Here then is the onset of the Oedipus complex in girls. It grows out of the castration complex and, according to Freud, the result is that "In girls the motive for the destruction of the Oedipus complex is lacking." It is not destroyed but either lingers throughout life or is slowly abandoned or repressed.

Thus in girls and women, Freud maintains, that there is no situation demanding the formation of a strong super-ego. The latter develops only gradually and seldom if ever reaches the heights it does in men. The contention that the female version of the innate Oedipus complex is destined simply to wither away, that therefore the feminine super-ego does not develop the sublimation of sexual energy that the male super-ego does, is Freud's rationale for the ideology of congenital male superiority and female inferiority.

He is a little abashed at announcing this doctrine to the world—as well he might have been, for it was formulated at a time when women throughout much of the world were fighting for equal political rights. The feminist movement was gathering great momentum and winning significant victories. After developing the above thesis on the inferiority of the super-ego of women, Freud says, "I cannot escape the notion (though I hestitate to give it expression) that for women the level of what is ethically normal is different from what it is in men. Their super-ego is never so inexorable, so impersonal, so independent of its emotional orgins as we require it to be in men. Character traits which critics of every epoch have brought up against women—that they show less sense of justice than men, that they are less ready to submit to the great necessities of life, that they are more often influenced in their judgments by feelings of affection or hostility—all these would be amply accounted for by the modification in the formation of their super-ego which we have already inferred." And he adds, "We must not allow ourselves to be deflected from such conclusions by the denials of the feminists, who are anxious to force us to regard the two sexes as completely equal in position and worth." [31]

Freud viewed the Oedipus complex as the central phenomenon in the childhood of both sexes, a phenomenon which ultimately determines not only the character and capabilities of the individual, but also the essential features of masculinity and femininity. He arrived at this view of human nature, as we have seen, primarily by means of discredited anthropological speculations and the translation of stereotyped symbols of an assumed inborn primordial language. By these dubious means he examined "the first manifestations of the patient's innate instinctual constitution" which led "into dark regions where there are as yet no sign-posts." He feels that these findings "would be of great importance if they could be proved to apply universally." [32] But he is never sure of his "discoveries" and is apparently fully aware of their shadowy, incomplete and unsatisfactory nature.

For example, of this theory of female development he says, "It must be confessed, however, that on the whole our insight into these processes of development in the girl is unsatisfactory, shadowy and incomplete." [33] In spite of such reservations and doubts Freud proceeds to treat the innate Oedipus complex and the details of its hereditary unfolding not only as established facts but as the central phenomenon of human life and the central doctrine of psychoanalysis. So far is this the case that, speaking of the complex, he says, "Its recognition has become the shibboleth which distinguishes the followers of psychoanalysis from its opponents." [34]

We have now examined Freud's phychoanalytical solutions to the two main problems of psychology—the origin and development of mind in the human species and in the individual human being.

Freud's psychology had its origins largely outside the mainstream of psychological thought. It attempted to leap the hiatus in man's knowledge of the organ of thought, emotions, "instincts," personality and character, namely the human brain. In doing so, it ended as it began, outside the mainstream of psychological science. Freud's psychoanalytical psychology has never been accepted by academic psychology. It has been almost universally repudiated and held in utter contempt by the vast majority of professionally trained psychologists.

At the same time, however, it has gained wide favor and influence in popular, non-professional books on psychology and in non-psychological fields such as literature, drama, the movies, television, the arts, anthropology, psychiatry, medicine, education and child-development. Through these diverse media, it has entered the popular mind as a powerful "cultural" force. Had this not been the case, had the verdict been left to the developing science of psychology, Freud's system would long since have been relegated to the oblivion especially reserved for non-testable speculative theories.

The material Freud presented was peculiarly suited for dramatic exploitation—sex, murder, incest, perversion, a formula for character development and for inter-personal relationships, and a pervasive symbolism. At the same time it constituted one of those forces combining to break up the false morality, hypocrisy and prudery of the Victorian nineteenth century. With all this behind it, it is understandable that it overcame its disadvantage and went on to become the dominant popular psychology on the American scene.

We have now to confront Freud's psychology by that science which has begun patiently to fill the hiatus over which Freud impatiently tried to vault—Pavlov's science of higher nervous activity applied to the two main problems of psychology.

Chapter IX

PAVLOV'S APPROACH TO THE TWO MAIN PROBLEMS OF PSYCHOLOGY

WE TURN NOW to an examination of Pavlov's solution of the body-mind problem, the science of higher nervous activity, in action, in search of answers to two key psychological questions; the development from animal behavior to human mind and from infant behavior to adult mentality.

Pavlov consistently employed two main aspects of the theory of evolution in all his experimental work: The process of adaptation within a given species to its environmental conditions of life; and the development of new species from old. More specifically, he investigated adaptive behavior in *higher* animals—dogs and apes—primarily in order to throw light on the origin and development of the *highest* species of the genus animal, namely man. In this he was concerned with both the continuity and the discontinuity, the underlying basic identity and the great qualitative difference.

From his work in the laboratory and the clinic, he concluded that there is a fundamental *"phylogenetic division of the brain."* [1] There are anatomical structures and physiological functions of the brain *common* to higher animals and human beings. And there are structural and physiological features *peculiar* to man. Dogs, apes and man have in common: *Anatomically,* the sub-cortical centers (and, of course, the lower parts of the brain) and the cerebral cortex; and, *physiologically,* the unconditioned reflex system (including chain reflexes or "instincts") and the conditioned, sensory reflex system of signalling reality. Man has *in addition* a greatly expanded cerebral cortex, the newest structures of which are concerned with the physiologically highest functional system, the speech or language system of signalling reality. In these features lie the basic identity and great qualitative difference between the nervous systems of higher animals and man.

The *animal* structures and systems are the result of millions of years of adaptation to *natural* environmental conditions of life. The structure of the sub-cortical unconditioned reflex system and of the cortical, sensory conditioned reflex system together comprise the hereditary nervous legacy to man from the animal kingdom. The additional structure of the human cortical speech system is the result of approximately one million years of adaptation to *social* environmental conditions of life, including social labor with tools and social living in communities.

Do Animals Think?

In his later years Pavlov experimentally investigated the behavior of anthropoid apes, and an examination of this work should illucidate his conception of the identity and difference between animal nature and human nature. More specifically, we are here concerned with the question: Do animals *think* and if so in what way is this thinking similar to, and in what way is it different from, human thinking? Pavlov performed his experiments with apes within a context of polemics against Robert Yerkes and Wolfgang Koehler, animal psychologists, the former an American, the latter a German.

According to Pavlov, Yerkes and Koehler in their interpretation of the behavior of apes had in effect worked out a new formula in defense of *dualism*. Under the impact of the conditioned reflex theory, they had admitted that the latter may account for canine behavior, but that neither association nor its physiological mechanism, the conditioned reflex, could explain the complex activity of anthropoid apes. Yerkes, and especially Koehler, maintained that, in addition to conditioned-reflex association, apes exhibit a "near-human faculty" of what they called "insight." Pavlov charged them with attempting to make a qualitative distinction between dogs and other such animals on the one hand, and apes and man on the other; the associationist-physiological-evolutionary approach, they maintained, may be able to account for the former, but certainly not for the latter.

Pavlov was highly incensed at this "declaration of war," as he termed it, on his attempt finally to disprove and dissipate the anti-scientific, idealist doctrine of dualism. The Yerkes-Koehler attack came at a time when, as Pavlov put it, "We have just begun more or less to liberate ourselves from dualism. The human mind has for a long time been a prisoner of idealistic concepts." At the very time when human beings could be liberated from the last great stronghold of idealism, the dualism of body and mind, scientists themselves rally to its defense by constructing a new rationale for it. Why do they do this? Pavlov answers that they are "under the spell of the dualistic world outlook."[2] The dualistic outlook is a powerful one, indeed, for it has the backing of the dominant tradition in human thought, including all organized religion. It is *the* accepted and acceptable doctrine and throughout much of the world it is the official or unofficial creed of state as well as church or temple. There are many forceful reasons why a scientist embraces dualism, not least of which is the fact that in so many cases it is likewise a cardinal feature of his own world outlook. But as Pavlov says, the scientist forfeits his claim to the proud title if he forgets "that his general world outlook should not be brought into scientific thought."

The science of higher nervous activity with the conditioned reflex as its central mechanism collides head-on with dualism. For it is a *monistic* conception of man as highly organized matter in motion, which in the form of the brain has achieved the highest evolutionary function (or property or quality) of mind or thought or consciousness. The stake in dualism is high—age-old individual as well as institutional *beliefs* on the one hand, and carefully nurtured *ignorance* at the hands of those who would benefit from it on the other.

It is not a subject of wonder or amazement, then, that Pavlov's science of the higher parts of the brain, the seat of the human mind, is literally all but unknown over the greater part of the earth's surface.

The new rationale for dualism provided by Koehler, Yerkes and many other psychologists including certain behaviorists, associationists and gestaltists, is directly or indirectly aimed at *neutralizing* the conditioned reflex theory of higher nervous activity. The method is greatly to oversimplify the function of the cerebral hemispheres by, as Pavlov put it, "reducing it to the simplest scheme of a physiological textbook, which merely shows the indispensable connection between the stimulation and its effect—and nothing more."[3] The cortex and its mode of functioning, the conditioned reflex, are viewed simply as a mechanism for making connections between the stimulus and the response. It ignores such processes as synthesis and analysis and irradiation and concentration. Such a mechanism could by no means account for even the simplest aspect of the highly complex behavior of either dogs or apes. This constitutes, of course, a ridiculous distortion of Pavlov's science, as even the severely limited discussion of it in the present volume serves to indicate. To reduce this experimentally established science back to its historic point of origin, the simple conditioned connection, is a travesty. Such, however, has been its fate to date over much of the world and especially in the United States.

Koehler and Yerkes serve merely as good examples of this process of the reduction of Pavlov's science to its lowest denominator. They performed experiments with anthropoid apes in which the apes in order to reach food had to overcome obstacles and perform certain feats. Up to a point, Koehler and Yerkes maintained, the apes proceeded by "trial and error" but then they "went off," sat down and "meditated at leisure" until they had an *"insight"* into the situation whereupon they got up and quickly solved the problem.

In his work with apes Pavlov reproduced the Koehler and Yerkes experiments, and found that the entire observed complex behavior could be accounted for in terms of association in which the underlying nervous mechanism was the conditioned reflex in all its refined and subtle forms of adaptive activity. In these experiments, Pavlov says, "We found nothing, absolutely nothing, that had not already been studied by us on dogs. This is a process of association followed by analysis effected with the help of analysers and accompanied by an inhibitory process which facilitates differentiation and rejection of that which does not correspond to the given conditions. Nothing more than this was observed by us in the course of our experiments. Consequently, there are no grounds for affirming that apes have some kind of 'intelligence' which brings them closer to man, while dogs have not and are capable only of an associative process."

Pavlov's point is not that apes are not *more* intelligent than dogs, but that the associative process, including sensory and cortical analysis, *is* intelligence in both apes and dogs. Koehler limits association simply to "trial and error" and makes intelligence into something mystical that happens in apes but not in dogs, when the former turns away from the problem and sits, supposedly "meditating."

From his own experiments, Pavlov concludes that the *turning-away-and sitting*, which actually does often occur, is the result of nervous fatigue from the *work* of association and analysis, which is *hard work* for the ape, and far from being "meditation" is actually *rest* from associative activity. The fact that the ape may, on occasion, solve the problem after such rest, does not indicate that he was thinking during the interval, but that being rested he can more quickly complete the required work of association and analysis. Irradiating inhibition brought on by fatigue rests the cortical cells — such is Pavlov's explanation of Koehler's "sitting and quietly meditating." "It turns out," Pavlov says, "that nothing but the silent inaction of the ape proves its intelligence!"

Pavlov, however, is far from asserting that the ape does not *think* or is not "intelligent." Rather he insists that association and analysis, all the great complexities of the conditioned reflex, sensory signalling, cortical linking, activity in fact actually constitute thinking. Thinking is nothing but such activity; and the product of the association-analysis (the thinking) is intelligent behavior. He accuses Yerkes and Koehler of dismissing association, which really explains intelligence, and making the latter into an inexplicable subjective phenomenon called "meditation" leading to "insight."

As a matter of fact, there is, according to Pavlov, a genuine type of meditating carried on by the ape, and by other higher animals including the dog, only it is not opposed to association; it is another and higher form of association. Here he refers to the fact that the ape sometimes momentarily looked away from the concrete problem situation, and then upon looking back solved the particular task at hand. The explanation is that traces forming memory images were associated or analyzed or both while the ape looked away from the actual objects themselves. According to Pavlov, apes and dogs and all higher animals carry on two types of rudimentary thinking: First, *thinking in action* in which the actual sensory images of actually present physical objects are the subjects of cortical association (or synthesis) and analysis; and second, *thinking in memory images* in which *traces* persisting in cortical cells are the subject of cortical association and analysis, Koehler mistakes this *thinking in action* as "trial and error" and *thinking in memory images* as "insight."

Koehler, whatever his intent, in effect conceals the mechanism of thought and intelligence and thus perpetuates the mystery of mind. "Naturally, the only explanation for such reasoning," Pavlov says, "is that Koehler is a confirmed animist, he simply cannot become reconciled to the fact that this soul can be grasped by hand, brought to the laboratory, and that the laws of its functioning can be ascertained on dogs. He does not want to admit this." [4]

Association and analysis together constitute thinking in action and in memory and their product is greater precision in adaptation to environmental conditions of life. The more permanent of these temporary conditioned linkages, the outcome of the process of analysis, are brought to bear on appropriate future occasions and thus constitute the fund of "knowledge" available to the dog or ape. Association is the overall process of thinking; while analysis is the refinement, the pin-pointing of associations so that they more accurately correspond to external reality. Such correspondence is the essence of *truth*. Thus the product of animal thought is *true knowledge* or *reflection* of the world in the animal *mind*. Mind, here, is not simply synonymous with *brain*, but is a legitimate term indicating the *functioning* of the brain, that is, the *current* processes of thinking in action and in memory (association or synthesis and analysis) together with the fund of *past* thinking, namely knowledge. Previously formed associations, which have been *tested* in action over a period of time and have been found to correspond with reality (having led to food, for example), comprise the elements of truth and knowledge. Thus mind is the inclusive, general term denoting the present and past cortical linkages, temporary connections or associations, the functional activity of the sense organs and the cerebral cortex, in higher animals. Mind is not *reduced* to the matter-in-motion of the senses and the brain, rather it is viewed by Pavlov as a product, a function, a property, a quality of matter in motion in the form of sensory and cerebral activity. In essence, animal mind or intelligence is the ever more exact reflection of the external environment in the form of acquired and tested temporary connections, linkages, associations or conditioned reflexes of the brain, and, more precisely, of the cerebral cortex.

On the basis of his experimental investigation, Pavlov says, "I am fully convinced that thinking is an association and I challenge anyone who disagrees with me to prove the contrary." [5]

He viewed this concept of mind as being *common to higher animals and man alike*. In dogs, apes and human beings, mind signifies the present and past acquired conditioned reflex connections or associations, elaborated through analysis and synthetically combined into chains and dynamic stereotypes or systems. According to him, both the animal and human mind represents knowledge of definite objects and relations existing in the external world. In each case the nervous mechanism is the sensory-cortical conditioned connection or association with all its elaborate synthetic and analytical activity. Knowledge is the *product* of thought, and thought is the *process* of association in animal and man alike. In each one, *intelligence* or *insight* is thinking-in-action employing relevant previously acquired associations (thought or knowledge) and forming new ones as required.

Koehler made a sharp distinction between dogs on the one hand and anthropoid apes and man on the other. Canine behavior, according to him, can be accounted for in terms of association, the conditioned reflex; but the complex behavior of ape and man can be accounted for only by the assumption of inexplicable "intelligence," "meditation" and "insight." Pavlov, on the contrary, attributed intelligence, meditation and insight to dogs, apes and man and explains them in terms of the sensory and cortical processes of association, the synthesis and analysis of conditioned reflex and other temporary connections.

Pavlov viewed the investigation of the behavior of dogs and apes as a step in gaining understanding of the human mind. "Thus we clearly witness," he says, "the formation of our thinking, we see all the reefs it encountered on the way, and all its methods."[6] This, however, does not mean the identity of the minds of man, ape and dog. It does not mean that Pavlov reduces the human mind to the animal mind. This is only the first half of the process of understanding the mind of man, the half that seeks to establish the *common* elements, those that man shares with his evolutionary ancestors. After all, human beings *sprang from* the higher animals; as a matter of fact, we *are* higher animals; the highest of the higher. Just as there are *structual* similarities in the brains of animals and human beings, so there are likewise *functional* cerebral (mental) similarities. It is this that Pavlov established in his experimental work with dogs and apes.

The second half of the task is to determine the *differences* between animal and human thinking or cerebral functioning. What is the great qualitative difference between human and animal associative conditioned reflex activity? That is how the problem presents itself to Pavlov.

In the first place, Pavlov disposes of Koehler's distinction between the *dog* and the *ape* by attributing the unquestionable difference to the ape's possession of *hands* rather than to an essential difference in cerebral or mental processes. Thus Pavlov viewed the differences between dogs and apes as basically *quantitative*—*more* associations and more refined analyses, and *more* cortical cells with *greater* development of the motor area resulting from the possession and use of hands in examining and manipulating the external environment.

The difference, however, between dogs and apes on the one hand and human beings on the other is *not* purely quantitative; it is not simply a matter of *more* associations, *mo*re refined analysis, *more* cortical cells or *more* developed cortical areas. It is all this, but it is at the same time a difference in *kind* of associations, together with corresponding new cortical areas.

Human beings, like apes, have hands; these hands, however, are far more highly developed and are used not solely for examination and manipulation of the environment, but are employed primarily to handle tools, and later, machines, with which to change the environment to meet human needs. The labor process, always a social one, requires language at least in the form of speech. People living and working together in communities, transient or otherwise, for a million years led not only to tremendous *expansion* of cortical areas and functions common to animals and man, but also to new cortical areas concerned with the new function of speech activity. "We, humans, in addition to the diverse movements of our hands," Pavlov says, "possess a complex of speech movements." [7]

The development of spoken language, characteristic of all peoples everywhere, made possible not only *more* associations, but a new *kind* of associative activity. Since according to Pavlov associative activity in general *is* thought, association of words does not consitute the essence of thought, but rather a *new kind* of thought, a specifically *human* form of thinking—verbal, generalized and abstract.

For Pavlov, then, *mind* with its primary attribute, thought, is synonymous with the associative, temporary reflex *functioning* of the cerebral hemispheres in higher animals, including man. This cerebral functioning consists in the nervous work of establishing, maintaining and perfecting a most delicate correlation between the organism and the environing world. This is for him the whole meaning of the term *mind*. It is not a "thing," a substance. It is a definite function. *Mind* is the functioning of the highest parts of the brain in the life-long process of adaptation to the conditions of life. Temporary connections or associations (including the nervous process of excitation and inhibition, synthesis and analysis, irradiation and concentration) comprise the mode of functioning of the cerebral hemispheres. Thus the term *mind* has a definite meaning—the associative linking activity of the cerebral hemispheres in the process of adaptation of animals and man to the conditions of their life. The *human* mind differs qualitatively from the mind of higher animals in the functioning of the second system of signalling reality, the speech system. The speech system is, in essence, a great refinement in the cerebral function of adaptation—one which, together with its progenitor, the labor process, makes possible the reversal of the adaptive function; the adaptation of the environment to human needs, desires and aspirations. But in any case "the mind is a most delicate correlation between the organism and the surrounding world"—nothing more nor less in animal or man.

Mind is a *function* of highly organized matter—the higher animal, including the human brain. "If all our relations with the surrounding world, even the most delicate ones, are nothing but our physiological brain," Pavlov says, "then there is no room for any other interpretation of the word 'mind.' And this is the kernal of the contradiction."[8] It is the kernal of the contradiction between the monistic materialist and the dualistic idealist approach to mind.

The identification of *mind* with the *cortical function* of establishing, maintaining and perfecting a most delicate correlation between the organism and the surrounding world in no sense whatever limits the mind of man—technology, science, art, literature, ethics, morality, all human culture, are, in this view, important functions of the brain in the never-ending process of adaptation in its specifically human form of changing the world and man to meet his own specifications and aspirations.

The mind of man is finally itself becoming the subject of *objective* investigation. Conceiving of mind in terms of cerebral functioning makes this entirely possible. A certain amount of progress has already been made along these lines, following the objective physiological methods of Pavlov. Certain of the phases and phenomena of child development and education have been investigated according to these methods. As yet it is a bare scratching-of-the-surface, but a vast program of research is projected which should, in the foreseeable future, fill in the gaps. We turn now to an examination of some of this work and some of this projected program in the application of Pavlov's science of higher nervous activity to the solution of the psychological problem of the origin and development of the individual mind.

Infant Mind to Adult Mind

The traditional psychological approach to the human mind was to give an account of the mental properties or capacities—

sensation, perception, attention, memory, imagination, thought, will and personality—together with their common correlations, and to make a descriptive study of the evolution of these qualities and capacities in the child. Such *descriptive* work, based on observation, was, of course, a necessary and important stage in the development of the science of psychology.

It was Pavlov's contention, however, that psychology had, at least by 1900, completed this initial preparatory stage of classification and phenomenal description and was ready to proceed to the second stage, rational explanation based on the objective experimental method of science. It was now a question, he maintained, of discovering the real functional mechanisms of this or that psychic quality, property or capacity. He was convinced that this must constitute the principal path of psychological research. Only in this way, he held, could psychology make the transition from classification to explanation and thereby be transformed into a mature science on an equal footing with other sciences. And only in this way could psychology fulfill its obligations to the study of child development and education, in turn making possible their transition from the descriptive to the explanatory stage, from immature to mature sciences.

Wholly occupied as he was in the later years with his work in the laboratory and the clinic, Pavlov himself was unable to carry out the research program he had outlined for psychology. This program is scarcely yet being given the attention it deserves.

Pavlov, his co-workers and followers did, however, do a considerable amount of work on a central problem in psychology, namely, perception, concerned with the origin and development of this mental capacity in the child.

The newborn infant is, of course, dominated by unconditioned reflexes such as sucking, swallowing and evacuating, elementary defense, orientation, and freedom reflexes. But from the very beginning *sensations* play a vital role. At first they simply set in motion, as has previously been noted, the unconditioned responses. Any object *touching* the lips initiates the appropriate sucking response. Without sensation there is no unconditioned reflex. What then is a *sensation?*

Pavlov answers that sensations are a function of the analysers. An analyser is a complicated piece of nervous apparatus consisting of three elements: (1) the receptor, an external receiving organ (ear, eye, skin, etc.); (2) a conducting nerve path; (3) the cerebral end of this nerve conductor in the cortex (not any one point in the cortex, but thousands of cells which are concentrated especially thickly in a given region, for example the visual cells in the occipital region). The process of sensation takes place only when the nervous impulse, which began in the stimulation of the receptor organ (e.g., the skin), has moved along the nerve fibre and reached the appropriate cells of the cerebral cortex. There, in the case of an infant, an inborn connection is made between the sensation (the activated cells of the given cortical area) and the appropriate cells of the motor area of the cortex. When an infant is accidentally pricked by a diaper pin, he will become rigid, hold his breath and then begin to cry and to thrash about in random movements. These would be innate unconditioned connections between two cell groupings of the cortex—the given receptor cells and the specialized motor cells.

<u>Sensation is the first</u> and most elementary <u>stage of "cognition."</u> In its *pure* form it is found only in the first days or perhaps weeks of the newborn infant's life. In this stage there is no recognition of external objects; there is only innate reaction to external stimuli in terms of the effect on the organism, pleasure or pain.

From very near birth, however, temporary connections are formed between a multitude of external stimuli and the few unconditioned stimuli. At first these conditioned connections are almost random, but gradually those that find no reenforcement are inhibited while those that are reenforced become more and more stable. Over a period of time, the more stable connections form linkages and these linkages are organized into dynamic stereotypes. These systems of acquired cortical connections are brought into action by stimulation from the peripheral (and internal) receptors. Now, however, instead of giving rise to sensations, the latter are analyzed and interpreted by an entire complex of cortical connections which transform the sensation into perception. The impulses from several sense receptors are correlated, broken down, analyzed and fitted into the already existing appropriate cortical systems and then synthesized into a motor act or an expression of emotion or both.

As the infant lives its day by day life in the social setting of the family, he acquires experience (conditioned connections temporarily stabilized into linkages and dynamic stereotypes and systems) in the light of which *all* his sensations are "interpreted." Such interpretation, past experience brought to bear on present experience, is the essence of *perception*. Thereafter pure sensation is all but impossible. Whether there is ever absolutely pure sensation is open to question. At any rate, soon after birth, the infant achieves the second stage of cognition, perception. Perception involves recognition of the external object and, as time goes on, more and more *knowledge* of its properties.

The nervous *mechanism* of perception in the pre-language child is identical with that of all other animals of any age, young or old. The primary difference, and it is a tremendous one, is the *social* environment of the child. He acquires much human knowledge (cortical linkages and systems) of the world from his family—what is edible and what not, what is dangerous, and a wide range of socially acceptable behavior and of human emotions. With all this, however, the nervous *mechanism* remains at the animal-infant level.

Only with the development of language, at first auditory and then spoken, does the child's mechanism of perception become specifically human. The third stage of cognition of the world is *verbally* conditioned perception.

Throughout his pre-language life, the child develops more and more discrimination in perception. But with the acquisition of language, perception takes a great leap forward in complexity and sensitivity. While a pre-language child and a higher animal of any age can be made to isolate, through analytical inhibition, any quality of an object, they cannot abstract that quality from the object and react to it independently of the object. For example, an infant and a dog both can be made to react to a red card while inhibiting reactions to cards of any other color (through the by now familiar process of reenforcing the red card while omitting to reenforce all cards of other colors). In this way a discriminatory conditioned connection is established to red cards, and a conditioned inhibition to others. But neither the pre-language child nor the dog can carry over the conditioned response to another red object, for example a red vase or a red dress. An attribute can be isolated from an object only by a conditioned connection with a word signalling it. Having acquired language, the child divides off or abstracts from an object a quality named by a word designating a color, a sound, weight, temperature, odor or taste. Speech separates the appropriate attribute from the object with which it was combined in the original perception.

The mechanism of verbal designation giving rise to generalization and abstraction is the temporary connection. If a word repeatedly accompanies the perception of one and the same attribute in different objects, then it gradually becomes a signal of this attribute regardless of the object. The audible (and later the visible) word constantly reenforces the perceived attributes (color, taste, etc.) and makes it possible to seperate it from the object itself. The attributes red, heavy, sweet, sharp, become knowledge of an objectively existing fact.

Thus perception is different in the post-language child. The inclusion of speech reorganizes the activity of the first or sensory system of signalling reality, greatly expanding and refining its sensitivity and powers of discrimination. The child or the adult recognizes the quality he has abstracted and named in any new object because the word is a generalized signal standing for *any* instance in which it occurs. The word makes possible the abstraction of the quality from all particular objects and thereby renders it perceptible in any object whatever. The word becomes a generalizing signal of a definite quality which the child at once divides off even in an unfamiliar object.

Language plays the part of a tool analyzing, synthesizing and generalizing a multiude of varied shades, scents and sounds. Those that correspond with relatively stable features of objective reality are constantly reenforced in the course of life, while those that do not are inhibited and extinguished as conditioned reflexes. Every verbal designation of a quality of an object reveals to the child a new aspect, a new attribute of the object, and the object is reflected in the child's mind ever more accurately, more fully and more significantly.

A decisive step in the transition from infancy to childhood is, then, according to Pavlov, the activization of the speech system of higher nervous activity. The isolation of some quality or other as an attribute of an object is what decisively marks off adult perception from the perception of infants; at the same time it likewise marks the great gulf between human and animal perception. An eagle may see farther and a dog detect a fainter scent than man, but neither can distinguish a fraction of the attributes of objects easily recognized by means of the human analyzers with their verbal signals. Speech provides that objects are known and recognized through their qualities, properties and attributes, and that they can be compared and classified and described in detail. Further, speech allows man to discern the slightest changes in the attributes of objects; to discover the course of the changes through observation; to bring about changes through production and through experimentation; and to determine causal relationships.

Human perception, the unity of language and sense experience, or in terms of higher nervous activity, the organizing of the sensory system by the speech system of signalling, is the basis for all human thought, all conception, all judgments, all science and all art. It is the fundamental psychic quality, underlying all others, which develops with the acquisition of language as the infant grows through childhood and enters maturity.

Perception then is a wholly *acquired* or *ontogenetic* mental capacity. Since the condition for its formation is social living, together with the hereditary structure of the human cerebral hemispheres, all peoples everywhere, at whatever stage of historical development, acquire the psychic quality of perception. The *degree* and type of development of this cerebral function, the extent to which perception is formed in the course of life, depends primarily on two conditions; the level of historical development of the society in which the child and adult live; and, the endless welter of accidental conditions surrounding each individual person. These two conditions, it will be noted, have nothing whatever to do with innate capacity, but only with external conditions of life.

Furthermore, perception continues to be formed during the entire life of the individual and can and does change with changed conditions of life. The sole *innate functions* of higher nervous activity are the limited number of unconditioned reflexes, which from birth become covered, raised and transformed into complex and fused reflexes and systems of reflexes involving predominantly acquired, conditioned reflexes.

Pavlov and his colleagues conclude that perception is a psychic quality which develops in the course of actual life in all human beings (with normal cerebral structure) but with great individual and ethnical differences. These functional differences, the differences in mental capacity, however, are wholly acquired and are highly fluid and subject to profound changes resulting from changed external conditions and internal resolve.

Recent experimental work by followers of the Pavlov theory and method in the science of higher nervous activity substantially supports the conclusion with regard to the acquired and changeable character of psychic qualities.[9] Investigation has as yet barely begun, but all indications point to verification of this fundamental Pavlovian hypothesis.

The experimental method of the conditioned reflex and an already vast and steadily increasing body of experimentally derived facts and laws of higher nervous functioning are available to all scientists. In addition there is a legacy of concrete problems awaiting controlled and careful investigation. Sufficient work has been done and knowledge amassed to put on the immediate agenda of psychology the discovery of the cerebral functional mechanisms of *all* the psychic qualities and capacities of the human mind. If and when psychology accepts the fully equal partnership of the physiology of the cerebral hemispheres, one of the most exciting and important stages in all the history of science will truly be initiated—man will discover at long last what he has sought throughout all his history, the nature of human nature. With this decision, man will make himself the subject of scientific investigation. To know himself has been his cherished goal for thousands of years. We are on the threshold. The tools are there, we have but to grasp them firmly. This Pavlov believed with all the passion of the dedicated scientist.

Today, twenty-three years after Pavlov's death, psychology and the physiology of the cerebral hemispheres are still not actively fused anywhere in the world. As late as 1950, leading Soviet scientists meeting in Moscow found it urgently necessary to exhort psychologists and cerebral physiologists to follow the advice and prognostication of Pavlov with regard to their fields. If this is the case in Pavlov's own country which takes an avowedly monistic-materialistic and militantly anti-dualistic-idealist approach, it is a striking measure of the power of traditional thinking on the subject of the human mind and its relation to the body. Dualism—*lip-service* to mind as a function of the brain while *acting* on the basis of its independence—it would appear still dominates, as Pavlov himself well knew, not only the popular mind but also the thinking of a great many scientists the world over.

In our country, as undoubtedly in others, there are individuals who are carrying on determined if always uphill struggles against dualism and on behalf of the unity of psychology and cerebral physiology. According to the testimony of Pavlov, this unaffiliated advance guard has the irresistible logic of all science on its side and sooner or later the fusion is "bound to be realized" and the problem of *mind* that has troubled mankind for so long "will find its real solution."

Today in all lands the fusion of psychology and cerebral physiology is on the agenda; but again in all lands, the actual fusion is an *ideological* issue. Traditional, age-old theological and dualistic modes of thinking do not surrender under the weight of evidence alone. The entire history of science, with its Galileos and Brunos, bears witness to the fact that great advances in verified knowledge require uncompromising struggles against old attitudes, prejudices and beliefs. If this is true of astronomy and physics, how doubly true it is when the science in question concerns man's most cherished illusion about the special position of his soul, his spirit, his mind, his own self.

The *separation* of psychology from cerebral physiology represents the last great theoretical stronghold of theology with its essential doctrines of the specially created human soul and its immortality. In the realm of science, dualism, in traditional or modern dress, furnishes the rationale and support for these theological doctrines. It is one thing to give lip-service, as all scientists at least must do, to the dependence of mind, soul, spirit on cerebral functioning. It is quite another thing to accept the experimentally established details of this dependence —for this means the final casting out of any lingering notion of *human exceptionalism* to the universal determinism of natural law.

Confrontation

The confrontation of the two psychologies presents a glaring contrast. The conclusion forces itself and scarcely need be stated.

It is undoubtedly true, however, that a similar confrontation of Freud's psychology by almost any other experimental approach would provide a contrast sufficient to render a verdict against psychoanalysis. Still the confrontation of Freud by Pavlov has one overriding advantage. The latter's science of higher nervous activity has at least begun the crucial task of filling the gap in human knowledge which historically made possible the Freudian type of speculative psychology.

If, as all science, rational thought and materialistic and scientific philosophy maintain, mind is the function of the brain, then it follows irrefutably that psychology, the science of mental processes, must be firmly grounded in knowledge of higher cerebral functioning. It is this knowledge which Pavlov, his colleagues, students and followers, have begun to give to the world. Lacking such a science, the psychologist has one of two general alternatives: First, to carry forward as far as possible, by means of objective experiments, the *descriptive and classificatory* investigation of animal or human behavior—leading to the accumulation of a vast body of facts and to statistical correlations; or second, to construct speculative, metaphysical systems on the basis of introspective observation and the probing of other minds by various means. A sufficient contrast will be possible whenever one of the latter speculative systems is confronted by one of the former statistical correlations of experimentally derived facts. Such a confrontation is itself sufficient to discredit any type of metaphysical psychology, including Freud's. But it is not sufficient to point the direction in which psychology must move if it is to make the transition from the inititial descriptive and classificatory stage of the science to the mature explanatory, causal stage

A primary prerequisite for such a transition is, according to Pavlov, a close alliance with cerebral physiology.* Pavlov's science, which is *Pavlov's* only in a generic sense, furnishes this prerequisite—even in its as yet initial and unfinished form. No longer is there any valid excuse for the dualistic practice of psychologists to pay lip-service to the principle of mind as a function of the brain and then to ignore the principle in all their work and exposition.

Freud, however, did much more than ignore the principle. Taking advantage of the current lack of a physiology of the cerebral hemispheres, he substituted an opposite principle, namely that mind, in spite of its established dependence on cerebral functioning, can be understood purely in terms of itself. Under the wing of this idealist principle he proceeded to construct what he called "the science of unconscious mental activity."[10]

Freud's is a psychology of The Unconscious. But The Unconscious is in effect Freud's substitute for the cerebral hemispheres. There being as yet no adequate physiology of the latter, he could proceed to pack the substitute with whatever he required in the construction of psychoanalysis, completely "unhampered," as he put it, by physiological facts and laws.

Any attempt to construct a psychology which flies in the face of the already established, if still growing, higher nervous physiology is beyond question doomed to failure. Freud's psychology is no exception to this principle. The principle is an amended version of the generally accepted one—honored mostly in the breach—that mind is a function of the brain. The amendment is the result of the long-awaited—and at the same time in some quarters greatly feared—birth of the science of the highest parts of the brain.

There may have been an excuse for Freud, as for his contemporaries, including William James, in the absence of this

* This does not by any means signify that psychology is synonymous with the physiology of the higher nervous activity. The latter is a prerequisite for the former. Psychology to become a science returns to certain other sciences as prerequisites also, namely a science of society and a scientific epistemology.

science. Although in the field of science itself, ignorance, even objective ignorance, cannot constitute ground for nullification of the scientific method and for resort to conjecture.

At any rate, our conclusion is that Freud's science of unconscious mental activity appears as a mythical substitute for the science of higher nervous (psychic) activity; to the temporary lack of which psychoanalysis owes its very existence.

We turn now to the *citadel* of psychoanalysis—psychopathology and psychotherapy. Does the science of unconscious mental activity stand up to the science of higher nervous activity any better in these fields than in psychology?

Chapter X
FREUD'S APPROACH TO MENTAL ILLNESS

BENJAMIN RUSH, SIGNER of the Declaration of Independence and father of American psychiatry, formulated in 1812 the basic principle which has become the cornerstone of scientific psychiatry the world over: Mental illness is "a derangement affecting that part of the brain which is the seat of the mind."[1]

In mental illness it is the brain that is ill, while the mind manifests symptoms in the form of disturbances of emotional and thought processes—disturbed behavior, fantasies, illusions, delusions and the like. Much of the history of psychiatry is the story of the search for the causes of cerebral disturbances. For some one hundred years psychiatrists firmly held to the belief that all mental illness was caused by organic lesions of the brain—damage to brain cells from injury or disease.

In the closing decades of the nineteenth century, however, a crisis developed. Although a great deal had become known with regard to organic lesions of the brain and the types of insanity associated with them, there remained numerous forms of mental illness in which no trace of actual brain damage or disease could be found. Some of these "uncaused" types of mental illness were clearly somatogenic and others psychogenic, but in neither case could any organic lesions be discovered.

Here was a lacuna in psychiatry. There appeared to be only two alternatives; either to give up the basic principle of psychiatry, and seek for purely mental causes, or to uphold the principle and continue the search for some minute and obscure, but as yet undetected lesions. On the one hand, by far the great majority of psychiatrists took the second alternative and stuck staunchly to their principle. They continued the fruitless search for organic lesions. On the other hand, a few psychiatrists and nuerologists, after some hesitation and soul-searching, abandoned the principle that the seat of mental illness lies in the higher parts of the brain, and turned to the disembodied mind itself as the source.

In our short story of Freud's life we saw that after considerable torment he chose the first alternative, abandoned the basic historical principle of psychiatry and set out to solve the problem of functional mental illness in purely psychological terms.

Pavlov, on the contrary, upheld the principle but at the same time rejected both alternatives. Instead of continuing the search for organic lesions, or seeking causes in the mind itself, he sought the solution in the science of the functioning of the cerebral hemispheres. Thus while Freud established a *psychopathological* approach to functional mental illness, wholly *outside* the mainstream of psychiatry, Pavlov established a *pathophysiological* approach squarely *within* its mainline tradition. We will now examine, in close juxtaposition, the respective outcomes of these two diametrically opposed approaches.

The best way, perhaps, to understand Freud's approach to functional mental illness is to trace its evolution in its author's mind. Psychoanalysis had a very interesting pre-history. In following the course of Freud's thinking, we will come to a fuller understanding of the psychological phenomenon which has had such a great influence on European and especially on American thought for half a century.

We related some of this story in outline in the chapter on Freud's life. Here we will trace it in more detail, for it is at once a highly instructive and fascinating tale.

By the time Freud had married and opened an office in Vienna (1886), he had already spent the better part of a year studying with Jean Charcot at the Salpêtrière in Paris. As a neurologist in private office practice, he was now confronted with the currently all but impossible task of treating neurotics. "I had attempted," he says, "to support myself and my rapidly increasing family by a medical practice among the so-called 'neurotics' of whom there were so many in our society. But the task proved harder than I had expected. The ordinary methods of treatment clearly offered little or no help: other paths must be followed. And how was it remotely possible to give patients any help when one understood nothing of their illness, nothing of the causes of their sufferings or of the meaning of their complaints?" Help was needed, "So I eagerly sought direction and instruction from the great Charcot in Paris. . . ."[2]

Freud reviewed his months of study with Charcot, and in 1893, on the occasion of the latter's death, he had an opportunity to summarize what he had learned from the aged master.

Charcot had been a great *classifier* of the multitudinous forms of organic mental illness by means of observation and post-mortem autopsy. In the closing years of his life he turned his attention to functional mental illness, and particularly to hysteria. He was the first to give medical status to hysteria and from that time on hysterical patients were no longer considered to be 'malingerers,' but to be suffering from a definite form of neurosis. Charcot not only classified the various types of hysteria but came to the conclusion that they were a manifestation of hypnoid states, or phases of hypnosis, involving a *dissociation* of consciousness. He distinguished three hypnoid phases corresponding to three phases of hysteria.

Thus Charcot arrived at a conclusion roughly similar to Pavlov's conclusion with regard to hysteria some forty years later. There was, however, a great difference. Pavlov's views on the relation of hysteria and the phases of hypnosis were drawn from his experimental work on hypnosis and nervous breakdowns in the laboratory together with clinical observations, and he was able to demonstrate the mechanism of hynosis and of the three phases (equalization, paradoxical and ultra-paradoxical) as intermediate states of irradiating inhibition intervening between wakefulness and full sleep. The dissociation of mental activity, discerned by Charcot and attributed to hypnoid states, was, according to Pavlov, the result of the abrogation of the regulatory and organizational role of the speech system of signalling, as a result of irradiating protective inhibition over areas of the cortex, and the consequent emotional and "instinctive" activity of the lower systems when released from regulation and organization.

The physiology of hypnotism and its phases was, of course, unknown at the time Charcot carried out his observations on hysteria. He could, therefore, only guess at the nature of the mechanism involved. And his guess was that the hypnoid states were the result of specific ideas holding sway in the mind of the patient. Of this guess Freud says in his article on Charcot, "With this the mechanism of an hysterical phenomenon was for the first time disclosed. . . ." [3]

As in the case of so many *masters* throughout the history of science and of thought, Charcot had made an historical discovery and at the same time a bad guess. He had discovered a close relationship between hypnotic phases and hysteria but had made a bad guess with regard to their mechanism. The *discovery* was made within the possibilities and limitations of the historical period, while the *guess* attempted to go beyond the possibilities and transcend the limitations. In actual fact, the kernal of truth discovered by Charcot could only be developed through discovery of the physiological mechanism of hypnosis —a feat accomplished by Pavlov only decades later.

In the meantime, the soon-to-be-famous disciples of Charcot —Pierre Janet, Alfred Binet, Joseph Breuer and Sigmund Freud, to mention only a few—almost entirely disregarded the kernal of truth in the master's teachings, and concentrated, rather, on the bad guess. The mechanism of hypnosis, they maintained, is the mechanism of hysteria, and this mechanism is purely mental, purely psychological; it is a specific idea, holding sway in the mind. From then on hysteria and all the other forms of neuroses, were considered by them to be purely mental phenomena to be analyzed and treated purely psychologically. Gone was the founding principle of psychiatry—that the brain is the organ of mental life and mental illness. "Charcot was the first to teach us," Freud says, "that we must turn to psychology for the explanation of the hysterical neurosis." [4]

The only trouble was that psychology at the time had nothing relevant to offer and as a result they had to rely on their own resources. "The psychology which ruled at the time in the academic schools of philosophy," Freud wrote, "had very little to offer and nothing at all for our purposes: we had to discover afresh both our methods and the theoretical hypotheses behind them." [5] But before he could proceed with the unfettered psychological approach, Freud had to free himself once and for all from the haunting conviction, consistently maintained by Charcot, that underlying the dissociation of consciousness and the specific ideas holding sway in hysteria, there was an organic cause.

Charcot always held that as the cause of hysteria there must be a temporary cortical lesion which had somehow disappeared by the time a post-mortem examination could be made. When Freud was at the Salpêtrière, Charcot had assigned him the task of making a comparison between organic cerebral paralysis and neurotic hysterical paralysis. Freud had not at the time been able to complete the assignment, but in 1893, soon after the master's death, he returned to the problem and published his findings in the form of a technical paper.[6] After discussing the various cortical lesions involved as mechanisms in organic cerebral paralysis, Freud asks, "What can be the nature of the lesion in hysterical paralysis?" Charcot held that it, too, was a *cortical* lesion, but functional or dynamic rather than organic. "Charcot constantly taught us," Freud wrote, "that it is a cortical lesion, but one of a purely dynamic or functional kind." Lack of knowledge of cortical functioning, however, prevented Charcot from determining the nature of a functional lesion of the cerebral cortex. All he could do was to insist that "there must be an hysterical (functional) lesion." Thus Charcot was never willing to give up the principle that the brain is the organ of mental life and mental illness. But passionate conviction was at the time as far as science could go. By now Freud had moved away from the conviction of his master and was ready to posit a purely mental "lesion," one entirely independent of nervous anatomy. "I maintain on the contrary," Freud wrote in this 1893 paper, "that the lesion in hysterical paralysis must be entirely independent of the anatomy of the nervous system."

Freud goes on, in the same paper, to say, "I shall now try finally to suggest what might be the lesion that causes hysterical paralysis." And he adds, "To do so, I only ask permission to pass over into the field of psychology." For this purpose, he goes back to Charcot's guess that the functional lesion is an idea, or complex of ideas, that holds sway in the mind and which is not associated with other ideas. The idea, according to Freud, is associated only with the memory of some traumatic experience and acts subconsciously to produce the symptoms of hysterical paralysis. If some idea "is attached to an association of great affective value it will be inaccessible to the free play of other associations. . . . This is the solution of the problem we raised; for in every case of hysterical paralysis we find that the paralyzed organ or the abolished function is engaged in a subconscious association endowed with great affective value. . . . The concept . . . is not accessible to conscious associations and volition because its entire associative affinity, so to speak, is saturated by a subconscious association with the recollection of the event, of the trauma, that produced the paralysis." [7]

Here in its earliest form is Freud's substitute for cortical functional lesions as the causal mechanism of neuroses. The substitute consists in a subconscious, or unconscious, association between an idea and a traumatic memory. Thus it is purely mental, with no reference to *cortical* functioning. This constitutes Freud's declaration of independence from the basic principle, not only of psychiatry but of all the life-sciences and of the age-old philosophy of science, materialism. From this point on, he is wholly outside the mainstream of psychiatry and of science as a whole, and has fully embraced the modern idealist doctrine of dualism in the form of psycho-physical parallelism. The bad guess of Charcot, taken apart from the old master's insistence on underlying functional lesions of the cerebral cortex, had become, by 1893, the cornerstone of Freud's thought.

In a paper likewise written in 1893, Freud, together with Joseph Breuer, developed still further the notion of the purely mental mechanism of neuroses. They maintained that the psychical trauma, the event which is the exciting cause of the illness, or the memory of it, acts continuously but subconsciously; and as long as it acts the neurosis will continue. The therapy indicated is to remove the memory of the event and thereby remove the neurotic symptoms.

This supposition of a continuously acting memory trauma in functional mental illness was taken over by Freud from a number of neurologists, psychiatrists and psychologists who were traveling in the same direction: Pierre Janet, Alfred Binet, Delboeuf, Möbius, Strümpel and Benedikt.

The notion of a continuously acting, unconscious memory is a gratuitous assumption made necessary if functional mental illness is to be viewed as purely mental. It is not accidental that *all* the various psychological theories of neurosis have this feature in common. It is the only likely alternative to the functional cerebral approach. For a purely mental etiology of neurotic states could only be constructed in terms of continuously acting memory-causes, which produce symptoms so long as they continue to operate. These memories are not known to the consciousness of the patient or anyone else, and so are held to be unconscious. They can be known only through the analysis, interpretation and symbol-translation of the subjective verbal content of neurotic fantasies, illusions and dreams. Thus everything depends on the translation of the so-called symbolic language of these borderline and pathological states. Such translations comprise the sole evidence for the existence of the so-called traumatic memory concepts.

Freud, as we have seen previously, tried several methods of probing the unconscious mind of his patients in an attempt to discover the traumatic memory-symbols supposedly underlying their neurotic symptoms—at first hypnotic commands and then hypnotic urging and suggesting. Finally he settled on three: the interpretation of dreams, free association, and transference phenomena. We have already discussed these methods, and will here concentrate on what Freud "found" by their means with regard to the purely mental mechanisms and causes of neurotic symptoms.

The results of his mind-probing were collected and correlated in two clearly defined periods. The first, from 1893 to 1897, belongs strictly speaking to the *evolution* of psychoanalysis, while the second from 1897 on, belongs to the *history* of psychoanalysis proper.

Freud's Childhood Seduction Theory of Neurosis and Its Collapse

The first period of "discovery" by means of the interpretive art of psychoanalysis ended in a grand fiasco which constituted a major crisis in Freud's life. In tracing or rather, as Freud, himself, called it, "constructing," the symbolic connections between the pathological symptoms on the one hand and the unconscious memory of the presumed traumatic event on the other, he was led further and further back into the life-history of the patient. Eventually all roads led to certain primal events in childhood. The memory of these events remained *unconscious* and the patients never recalled them. In eighteen cases of hysteria, however, Freud was able to convince the patients that his construction, built through the translation of dream and fantasy symbols, must have been the traumatic experience which ultimately caused their illness.

In all eighteen cases, the construction involved a passive sexual experience undergone in early childhood, from the age of one and one-half to eight or ten years old. "A passive sexual experience before puberty: this is the specific etiology of hysteria," Freud concluded. And he described this constructed event in more detail: "The event, the unconscious image of which the patient has retained, is a premature sexual experience with actual stimulation of the genitalia, the result of sexual abuse practiced by another person, and the period of life in which this fateful event occurs is early childhood, up to the age of eight or ten, before the child has attained sexual maturity." [8]

The "mental counterpart" of the traumatic premature sexual experience consists, according to Freud, in the reproduction of the primal event in the patient's psychic life as "memory-symbols of this experience." From the translation of the memory-symbols by means of "the art of interpretation or translation," Freud maintained, "the unconscious material (the passive sexual experience) may be reconstructed."

The mechanism of hysteria, Freud now held, involves the defense against the childhood traumatic experience through repression of its memory. The latter thus becomes an unconscious memory charged with sufficient psychic energy to force its way into expression in concealed and distorted symbolic form through dreams, fantasies and neurotic symptoms. Analysis traces this process backwards from the symbols to the reconstruction of the sexual event thus symbolized. Analysis must "lead the patient's attention from the symptom back to the scene in and through which it originated." The therapy consists in correcting the original emotional reaction to the childhood sexual experience, and thus dissipating (or abstracting) its affective energy. "And having thus discovered (the primal event)," Freud says, "we proceed when the traumatic scene is reproduced to correct the original psychical reaction to it and thus remove the symptom." [9]

Freud claimed great success for this analytic and therapeutic procedure. In a series of papers he proclaimed a whole new era in the investigation and cure of hysteria. He indignantly refuted the often repeated charges that he was forcing his constructions on the patients. "I have never yet succeeded," he insisted, "in forcing on a patient a scene that I expected to find in such a way that he appeared to live through it again with all the appropriate emotions." He marshalled pages and pages of arguments in defence of the reality of his childhood sexual constructions. The abuse poured out on him for his theories would fill volumes. Newspapers as well as technical journals joined in the wholesale condemnation of what were considered his "monstrous" views on childhood.

At this point Freud stood alone in the world, and had to take the universal repudiation of his "discoveries" without support from any source. Even his friend and collaborator Joseph Breuer broke with him over the issue of his childhood sexual theories. Freud later maintained that if he had not been a Jew and therefore accustomed to lonely persecution, he might himself have broken down at the time under the terrific pressure of outraged incredulity and highly charged condemnation. He called this period his "lonely years."

In the face of this universal opposition, Freud continued for several years to proclaim his discoveries as a great revelation. "I put forward the proposition, therefore," he wrote in 1896, "that at the bottom of every case of hysteria will be found one or more experiences of primitive sexual experience, belonging to the first years of childhood, experiences which may be reproducd by analytic work though whole decades have intervened. I believe this to be a momentous revelation, the discovery of a *caput nili* of neuropathology." By 1897, he had extended his sexual theory to include all forms of functional mental illness, not just hysteria: "Detailed investigations during the last few years have led me to the conviction that factors arising in sexual life represent the nearest and practically the most momentous causes of every single case of nervous illness."

Then came the dénouement. Freud's world collapsed around his head. His critics and accusers had been right all along. He had to admit at last that he had in fact forced his symbol-reading construction on his patients, that there was not a word of truth in his theory of infantile abuse and seduction as the cause of hysteria and other neurotic states. It was a bitter pill to swallow. "When this etiology broke down," he wrote later, "under its own improbability and under contradiction in definitely ascertainable circumstances, the result at first was helpless bewilderment. Analysis had led by the right paths back to these sexual traumas, and yet they were not true. Reality was lost from under one's feet. At that time I would gladly have given up the whole thing, just as my esteemed predecessor, Breuer, had done. . . ."[10] In his short autobiography he wrote: "Under the pressure of the technical procedure which I used at the time, the majority of my patients reproduced from their childhood scenes in which they were sexually seduced by some grown-up person. . . . I believed these stories, and consequently supposed that I had discovered the roots of the subsequent neurosis in these experiences of sexual seduction in childhood. . . . When, however, I was at last obliged to recognize that these scenes of seduction had never taken place, and that they were only phantasies which my patients had made up or which I myself had perhaps forced upon them, I was for some time completely at a loss. My confidence alike in my technique and in its results suffered a severe blow."[11]

The above statements were made by Freud almost a quarter of a century after what he called "the general collapse" of his "neurotica."[12] The debacle of his infantile seduction theory actually took place in 1897, but he withheld public retraction of it for eight years, or until 1905. The eight-year interval is a measure of his mortified shame and of his extreme reluctance to give the host of severe critics the satisfaction of witnessing his abject humiliation.

It is only in a letter to his one remaining friend at this time, Wilhelm Fliess, that we know of the 1897 collapse at all.

On September 21, 1897, he announced to Fliess: "Let me tell you straight away the great secret which has been slowly dawning on me in recent months. I no longer believe in my *neurotica*." He then goes on to list the reasons for his disillusionment: A great many patients "ran away" from the analysis; lack of the success which he had expected: and "the possibility of explaining my partial successes in other, familiar ways." He had claimed to have had remarkable cures by bringing the seduction scenes to consciousness. "Now," he wrote, "I do not know where I am. . . . Certainly I shall not tell it in Gath, or publish it in the streets of Ashkalon, in the land of the Philistines." He tried, nevertheless, to put up a bold front before his friend: "It is curious that I feel not in the least disgraced, though the occasion might seem to require it . . . but between ourselves I have a feeling more of triumph than of defeat, which cannot be right." He regretted only that his hope of sudden fame and fortune had been dashed: "The hope of eternal fame was so beautiful, and so was that of certain wealth, complete independence, travel, and removing the children from the sphere of worries which spoiled my own youth. All that depended on whether hysteria (neurotica) succeeded or not."

The letter closed with a note on which Freud's hopes were shortly to be reconstructed. "In the general collapse," he wrote, "only the psychology has retained its value. The dreams still stand secure, and my beginnings in metapsychology have gone up in my estimation." And he added significantly, "It is a pity one cannot live on dream-interpretation, for instance."[13] It is tempting to note that in the not-too-distant future Freud, the first of a legion, was to make a rather good living indeed on the interpretation of dreams.

The crisis of defeat coincided with Freud's decision to psychoanalyze himself. It was through this analysis that he painfully worked his way out of disillusion toward the final stage of his psychoanalytical approach to neurotic phenomena.

Freud's Self-Analysis and His Theory of Neurosis

Psychoanalysis proper is essentially a product of Freud's self-analysis. The analysis was undertaken in 1897, apparently for two reasons: The immediate cause was a mild hysterical neurosis from which he had suffered chronically ever since his student days but which had become intensified under the impact of the general collapse of his seduction theory; the ultimate reason was to salvage what he could from his past analytical work and to find a basis on which he could proceed purely psychologically to solve the problem of neurosis and treat his patients.

The record of this period is to be found only in a series of some eighteen letters written to Wilhelm Fliess between September, 1897 and September, 1898. The analysis proceeded almost exclusively through the interpretation of the symbols in his own dreams and so-called free-associations.

It begins with a complaint of strange, unconscious and neurotic states of mind. "Incidentally, I have been through some kind of a neurotic experience, with odd states of mind not intelligible to consciousness—cloudy thoughts and veiled doubts, with barely here and there a ray of light. . . . I believe I am in a cocoon, and heaven knows what sort of creature will emerge from it." A month later he writes, "I still do not know what has been happening to me. Something from the deepest depths of my neurosis has ranged itself against my taking a further step in understanding of the neuroses." The only thing he is still sure of is the interpretation of dreams. "So far as technique is concerned I am beginning to prefer one particular way as the natural one. The firmest point seems to me to be the explanation of dreams." He goes on to relate a recent dream of his own and in his interpretation traces the unconscious dream content back to childhood.

After another month has passed, he speaks of "the turbulence of my thoughts" and says that he is "tortured with grave doubts about the neuroses." After mentioning "my little hysteria," he confesses to Fliess for the first time that he is conducting a self-analysis. "After a spell of good spirits here I am now having a fit of gloom. The chief patient I am busy with is myself." And he remarks that "This analysis is harder than any other. . . . But I believe it has got to be done and is a necessary stage in my work."

Two months later, he writes, "Outwardly very little is happening to me, but inside me something very interesting is happening. For the last four days my self-analysis, which I regard as indispensable for clearing up the whole problem, has been making progress in dreams and yielding the most valuable conclusions and evidence . . . and so far I have always known where the next night of dreams would continue." There follows a lengthy analysis of several dreams from which he concludes: As a very young child he was sexually in love with his mother, had at the time seen her nude, and was jealous of both his father and his newborn sister, against whom he had entertained a death-wish and in consequence had suffered guilt feelings. These feelings became all but unbearable when his sister did in fact die a few months later.

Here in the symbol-reading translation of his own dreams is the first glimmering of the infantile construct that was to become the center of the psychoanalytic approach to neuroses. But he is not as yet satisfied: "I still have not got to the scenes which lie at the bottom of all this." He was looking for new traumatic infantile scenes which could replace the discredited abuse and seduction constructs.

In letter after letter he reports, in one set of words or another, that "Last night's dream produced the following . . ." and goes on to outline the dream and to give his interpretation of its symbols. Interspersed are statements to the effect that "My self-analysis is the most important thing I have in hand, and promises to be of the greatest value to me, when it is finished." As the self-analysis proceeds, its tempo increases, and likewise the pain and anguish. There are alternately moods of depression and elation as he discloses how his infantile sexuality had determined so much of his adult life. "I am living only for 'inner' work. It gets hold of me and hauls me through the past in rapid association of ideas; and my mood changes like the landscape seen by a traveller from a train. . . . Some sad secrets of life are being traced to their first roots. . . . days when I slink about depressed because I have understood nothing of the day's dreams, phantasies or mood, and other days when a flash of lightning brings coherence into the picture, and what has gone before is revealed as preparation for the present." At one point he remarks, "Since I have started studying the Unconscious I have become so interesting to myself"; and at another, "Under the influence of the analysis my heart-trouble is now often replaced by stomach-trouble."

At last there came a time when he could announce, "After the terrible pangs of the last few weeks, a new piece of knowledge was born in me." There follows in rapid succession the proclamation of several doctrines, the theoretical fruits of his self-analytical dream interpretations; the Oedipus complex, the infantile degenerative phases, resistance and repression.

First he proclaims the Oedipus complex. "Only one idea of general value has occurred to me, I have found love of the mother and jealousy of the father in my own case too, and now believe it to be a general phenomenon of early childhood, even if it does not always occur so early as in children who have been made hysterics. . . . If that is the case, the gripping power of *Oedipus Rex,* in spite of all the rational objections to the inexorable fate that the story presupposes, becomes intelligible, and one can understand why later fate dramas were such failures. . . . The Greek myth seizes on a compulsion which everyone recognizes because he has felt traces of it in himself. Every member of the audience was once a budding Oedipus in phantasy, and this dream fulfilment played out in reality causes everyone to recoil in horror, with the full measure of repression which separates his infantile from his present state."

Second, Freud announces the discovery of infantile sexuality, what he calls the degenerative phases, perverted tendencies of oral and anal eroticism in the very young child, revealed by symbol-translation from adult dreams and fantasies. Through reconstructing such tendencies in his own childhood he came upon the third of his major doctrines, resistance.

Evidently he put up a fierce resistance against himself when he was faced with the end product of his own translations. "An idea about resistance has enabled me to put back on the rails all the cases of mine which looked like breaking down, with the result that they are now going on satisfactorily again. Resistance, which is in the last resort the thing that stands in the way of the work, is nothing but the child's character, its degenerative character, which has, or would have, developed as a consequence of those experiences which one finds in conscious form in so-called degenerate cases; in these cases, however, the degenerative character is overlaid by the development of repression. In my work I dig it out, it rebels, and the patient, who started by being so civilized and well-mannered, becomes vulgar, untruthful or defiant, a malingerer. . . . Resistance has thus become an objectively tangible thing for me."

Thus far he has probed deeply into his own mind with the grappling hook of dream-symbol translation and come up with three of the four main elements of his final theory—the *Oedipus complex, infantile sexuality* and *resistance*. At this time he wrote to Fliess, "My own analysis is going on, and it remains my chief interest. Everything is still dark, including even the nature of the problems, but at the same time I have a reassuring feeling that one only has to put one's hand in one's own store-cupboard to be able to extract—in its own good time—what one needs." What he needed now was some psychical mechanism which would account for the defense of the ego against the shocking degenerative tendencies of infantile sexuality, against the incestuous phenomena of the Oedipus complex and against the later dreams, phantasies and moods based on them. "I only wish," he wrote to Fliess, "that I had also grasped what lies behind repression."

A month later he had once again put his hand in his own store-cupboard and this time had brought out the psychical mechanism of repression. Like resistance, it is "a question of the attitude adopted to former sexual zones." The zones referred to are, of course, "the regions of the anus and the mouth" which according to him play such a role in infantile sexuality. When memories based on these zones occur in adult life, the ego turns away from them in disgust. By analogy with "the sensations of smell," repression is the turning away in disgust at memories of what formerly were degenerative erogenous regions and incestuous erotogenic objects. "To put it crudely," Freud writes to Fliess, "the current memory stinks just as an actual object may stink; and just as we turn away our sense organ—the head and nose—in disgust, so do the preconscious and our conscious turn away from the memory. *This is repression.*"

Everything depends on the success, partial failure or complete failure of this mental turning away in disgust, namely, repression. The repression of the degenerative infantile sexuality and of the Oedipus complex is the key to health and illness.

It is thus no longer as it was in his seduction theory, *childhood genital experience* that produces neuroses. Rather it is the *infantile pre-genital experience,* the oral and anal, and incestuous scenes, together with the unconscious memories of them, which break through in neurotic dreams, fantasies, illusions, moods, etc. When these pre-genital phases and their memories have not been successfully repressed, when they are turned away from in disgust, but at the same time have not had their psychical energy sufficiently diverted to the genital zone or to sublimative activity (cultural, economic, social, etc.), or both, then there is produced "nothing but symptoms instead of purposive ideas." The etiology of neuroses is now viewed by Freud to be dependent on the manner and degree in which the abandonment of the infantile pre-genital zones (anal and oral) and the incestuous objects (mother, father, siblings) is accomplished, or whether it is accomplished at all (as in degenerates and perverts).

All the major elements of the psychoanalytical theory of neurosis are at last present. Freud's own store-cupboard of The Unconscious, opened with the magical key of dream interpretation, had indeed proved to be well stocked with what he needed. The rebirth of his purely mental approach from the ashes of the seduction theory was now complete.

It was about this time that he wrote to Fliess, "I can hardly tell you how many things I—a new Midas—turn into—filth. This is in complete harmony with the theory of internal stinking."

The closing letters of this series strike a high note of elation and self-confidence. "All sorts of little things are happening: dreams and hysteria are fitting in with each other ever more neatly." And he soon announces to his friend that he is writing *The Interpretation of Dreams,* his magnum opus. "I am deep in the dream book, writing it fluently and smiling at all the matter for 'head-shaking' it contains in the way of indiscretions and audacities." Finally he writes, "Self-analysis has been dropped in favor of the dream book." [14]

The self-analysis had served one of the two purposes for which it was undertaken, to rebuild his theory of neuroses from the shambles of the seduction collapse. It had, however, failed to remove Freud's neurotic symptoms—alternating moods of deep depression and intoxicated elation, and phobias such as fear of travel and of open spaces, together with various somatic and vegetative disturbances. As a treatment of neurotic states, Freud concluded that "self-analysis is really impossible." [15] Although the self-analysis was continued intermittently until his death, he had to learn to live with his "little neuroses."

Speaking years later of the crisis he had undergone, Freud said, "Perhaps I persevered only because I had no choice and could not then begin again at anything else. At last came the reflection that, after all, one has no right to despair because one has been deceived in one's expectations; one must revise them." And he goes on to summarize the *revision* he had made, and which he still maintained: "If hysterics trace back their symptoms to fictitious traumas, this new fact signifies that they create such scenes in phantasy, and psychical reality requires to be taken into account alongside actual reality. This was soon followed by the recognition that these phantasies were intended to cover up the auto-erotic activity of early childhood, to gloss it over and raise it to a higher level; and then, from behind the phantasies, the whole range of the child's sexual life came to light." [16]

On the basis of the revised approach, Freud was able to retain the sexual etiology of neuroses. Not seduction but phantasies built out of unconscious infantile-sexual memories constitute the essential element. Instead of the father, mother, sister, brother, nurse or governess seducing or attacking the infant Freud now maintained that it was the infant which was the would-be seducer. The infant displayed perverted sexual impulses toward father, mother, sister, brother, nurse or governess. These impulses were then suppressed and appeared later in phantasies, dreams and neurotic symptoms generally.

We are now in a position to investigate Freud's final conception of the purely psychical mechanism of neurosis. It is composed of two elements: First, a failure to master the real problems of life; and second, the innate infantile factor. The failure in life-situations results in a turning away from reality and the seeking of substitutive satisfaction in phantasy involving regression to memory-material from childhood and infancy. Thus the neurotic symptoms are viewed generally as *regression* backwards toward the first years of life. At the same time, the repressed infantile constitution together with the vicissitudes it underwent in a given particular childhood, operates in a forward direction pointing out to the regressing mind of the patient certain infantile paths it may take. Thus the psychical mechanism of neurotic states is viewed by Freud as being a combination of a backward and a forward mental motion which meet to construct the particular symptoms of the specific mental illness. But in this convergence, the hereditary infantile structure with its childhood impressions is the determining factor. It determines not only the path of phantasied substitute satisfactions, but whether and at what point the individual will in the first place fail to master the real problems of life, that is, it decides for or against neurosis, and the timing of the disease.

It was largely over the nature of this psychical mechanism that Carl Jung broke with Freud. Freud later charged that Jung had rejected the infantile factor, which is the heart of the particular Freudian psychoanalytical approach, and implied that he had done so in order to be more acceptable to puritanical American public opinion.

The infantile factor is, indeed, the central and distinctive feature in Freud's purely mental theory of neuroses. It is the basis of etiology, just as in the Freudian psychology it is the formulation of personality and character. We turn now to Freud's theory of neurosis in action as seen through his lengthy case histories.

Freud's Case Histories

So crucial was the question of the infantile factor that of his five full-length case histories (six hundred pages) two were selected as "proof positive" of the infantile-sexual etiology of neuroses—the case of "Little Hans" (1905) and the case of the Russian Nobleman (1909).

These cases were selected because they involved neuroses during early childhood. "The occurrence of a neurotic disorder in the fourth and fifth years of childhood," Freud says, "proves, first and foremost, that infantile experiences are by themselves in a position to produce a neurosis, without there being any need for the addition of a flight from some problem which has to be met in real life." In the two cases Freud maintained that "we discover nothing but instinctual trends which the child cannot satisfy and which it is not old enough to master." [17]

Actually, the same holds true, according to Freud, in the other three cases reported at length. The difference lies only in the fact that the neurotic symptoms appeared in adult life rather than in childhood. The infantile sexual element plays the decisive role in any case.

Conscious memory, does not extend back into the first years of life. Thus he cannot claim that patients *recall* experiences of this period. What he does do is to *construct* what must have happened, or should have happened, according to the theory of innate infantile-sexual phases. The primal scenes from one or more of the phases are considered as the real cause of the neurosis, at whatever age it develops. "These scenes from infancy," Freud says, "are not reproduced during the treatment as recollections, they are the products of construction." And he adds, "Many people will certainly think that this single admission decides the whole dispute." At least, we want to know *how* they are *constructed*. The answer is that they are built out of dream and phantasy symbol-translations.

For example, little Hans once witnessed, at close hand, a team of horses fall down and thrash about when trying to pull a heavily loaded van. As a result Hans developed a fear of horses (animal phobia) to the extent that he would not venture outside the house even with his governess. It seems that he was particularly afraid of draught horses and that heavy leather bridles had become associated with such animals. Freud's interpretation of this, and of course it is only one of many episodes and dreams in Hans' young life subjected to analysis, is that the heavy leather strap across the horse's nose and the eye-blinders were in fact symbols representing the moustache and eye-glasses of the father. So that fear of these horses was in fact fear of the father. This fear was connected, as read in other symbols, with a threat of castration by agency of the father, which in turn was connected—as the infantile theory required—with masturbation, which in turn was excited by erotic love of his mother, which in turn made him afraid of his father's wrath and revenge (again castration), which in turn made him still more afraid of horses, and so on.

Freud interpreted the falling down of the horses as exciting a death-wish on the part of little Hans against his father—an unconscious wish that his father should have such a fall. At the same time some of the symptoms were supposed to arise out of remorse and guilt for this particular death-wish. The to-a-child overpowering experience of being close to a team of horses when they fall, was at the beginning of the analysis dismissed by Freud as a cause of the little boy's fear. He viewed it only as the *exciting cause* which *triggered* the innate infantile-sexual mechanism.

The outcome of the case of little Hans, based on all the symbol translations and interpretations, culminating in the construction of the primal scene, was, according to Freud, that the four-year-old boy had homosexual tendencies (toward his father) with later traits of masculinity and polygamy (towards his mother, governess, and little girl playmates). The case came to an end when little Hans decided in phantasy to marry his mother while letting his father marry his grandmother (the father's mother). This signified, to Freud, not only the end of the presumed phobia (which is all but lost sight of in the course of the analysis) but also the giving up of homosexual desires for his father, on one side, and the death-wish and fear of his father on the other. After all, he chose his mother as his erotic, four-year-old love-object and magnanimously let his father marry his own mother, too.

In the course of the analysis little Hans often exploded with good sense, "Oh, do let me alone." At one point, when the mother had been berating herself before her husband for perhaps having unconsciously seduced her son, Freud remarks to him, "But she had a pre-destined part to play, and her position was a hard one." It was innately pre-ordained that Hans fall sexually in love with his mother and nothing she could have done would have avoided the fate. At another point, Freud remarks of Hans, "The little Oedipus is doing better than prescribed by destiny."

It is interesting to note that in the case of little Hans it was the father who carried on the analysis. Once a week he reported the details to Freud who in turn suggested what the father should be looking for. Both the mother and father were confirmed and devoted followers of psychoanalysis and had made a pact with Freud before the birth of their son that they would faithfully report his infantile sexual development. It was during the course of these periodic reports that little Hans developed his fear of horses.

The basis of the analysis, as of all Freud's work, was that a neurosis, like a dream never talks nonsense. "But a neurosis," he says, "never says foolish things, any more than a dream." Every image, every word, every emotion and every act means something. The problem of the analysis is to uncover the hidden unconscious meaning. This meaning is invariably an unconscious wish or motivation—as for example Hans' fear of horses falling down is interpreted in part as an unconscious deathwish against his father. The essential therapy is identical with the analysis. The aim of the therapy, as of the analysis, is to make unconscious wishes conscious. The object in both instances is accomplished by interpreting the hints thrown out in symbolic form by The Unconscious and then reconstructing the fated primal scenes out of the symbol-translations. "Therapeutic success, however," Freud says, "is not our primary aim; we endeavor rather to enable the patient to obtain a conscious grasp of his unconscious wishes. And this we can achieve by working upon the basis of the hints he throws out, and so, with the help of our interpretive technique, presenting the unconscious complex to his consciousness *in our own words.*" (Italics are Freud's.)

The hints from The Unconscious (dreams and phantasies) never say foolish things. As a matter of fact they are forced by the interpretation and by the imposition of the fated constructs (infantile phases and the Oedipus complex) to talk Freud's language. As he did in his own self-analysis, he puts his hand into the little patient's store-cupboard of symbols and finds what he needs and what he is looking for by means of symbolreading. On the basis of such a procedure one could amass an overwhelming mountain of observations to "prove" almost anything.

In psychoanalysis, the analyst first plants what he later reaps. This is true whether the patient be a child or an adult. Freud admits this point and admits also that it detracts from the evidential value of an analysis. "It is true," he says, "that during the analysis Hans had to be told many things that he could not say himself, that he had to be presented with thoughts which he had so far shown no signs of possessing, and that his attention had to be turned in the direction from which his father was expecting something to come. This detracts from the evidential value of the analysis; but the procedure is the same in every case. For a psychoanalysis is not an impartial investigation, but a therapeutic measure. Its essence is not to prove anything, but merely to alter something. In a psychoanalysis the physician always gives his patient (sometimes to a greater and sometimes to a less extent) the conscious anticipatory images by the help of which he is put in a position to recognize and to grasp the unconscious material."

"A psychoanalysis," Freud says, "is not an impartial scientific investigation," but he drew from it dozens of books purporting to contain impartial scientific generalizations and facts. The trouble is, he complains over and over, that only direct experience of an analysis, on the giving and taking side, will suffice to convince anyone of the validity of his findings. This is, indeed, a sad plight for any doctrine with pretensions to scientific value. "It is a regrettable fact," Freud says "that no account of a psychoanalysis can reproduce the impressions received by the analyst as he conducts it, and that a final sense of conviction can never be obtained from reading about it but only from directly experiencing it. But this disability attaches in an equal degree to analyses made upon adults." And one is tempted to add the same disability attaches to mystical experiences and the phenomena produced by mediums such as table tipping, extrasensory perception and contact with the nether world.

Little Hans is a model case to "prove" the decisive part played by the infantile factor in the etiology of neuroses. Of this case Freud writes, "I am aware that even with this analysis I shall not succeed in convincing anyone who will not let himself be convinced, and I shall proceed with my discussion of the case for the benefit of those readers who are already convinced of the objective reality of unconscious pathogenic material." In short, he proceeds for the benefit primarily of the analysts and for those who have already undergone analysis. And he adds,

"And I do this with the agreeable assurance that the number of such readers is steadily increasing." [18]

Freud, of course, analyzed innumerable cases in addition to his own and the five reported at length. In every instance he was able, he maintained, to trace the neurosis back to the infantile complexes to be found in little Hans and himself. "But the neuroses of these other patients," he writes, "could in every instance be traced back to the same infantile complexes that were revealed behind Hans' phobia. I am therefore tempted to claim for this neurosis of childhood the significance of being a type and a model, and to suppose that the multiplicity of the phenomena of repression exhibited by neuroses and the abundance of their pathogenic material do not prevent their being derived from a very limited number of processes concerned with identical ideational complexes." [19] The "identical ideational complexes" are, of course, the innate infantile phases and the Oedipus complex, together with their inter-relationships.

Psychoanalysis, as a method of treatment, is, according to Freud, limited to those cases which deviate from the normal in only a relatively slight degree. To benefit from analysis the patient must "possess a normal mental condition." Speaking of the conditions under which psychoanalysis is possible, he says, "And finally it is possible only if the patient is capable of a normal mental condition from the vantage point of which he may overlook the pathological material." In other words, Freud considered his method to be applicable primarily to ambulatory neurotics—those who could continue to live their normal lives but with more or less difficulty, pain and suffering.

In addition to the degree of illness, Freud sets another condition for admission of patients to analysis. After remarking that "my material does in fact consist of chronic nervous cases recruited from the more cultivated classes," he goes on to show that this was not wholly accidental. The most essential condition is that the patient be *educable,* by which Freud does not only mean that he must not be too ill, but that he must "possess a reasonable degree of education." The other condition is that the patient must have a great deal of time to put at the disposal of the analyst, plus ample financial resources. He considered that for a real and effective analysis years were required, years in which the patient met with him for one hour each day, month in and month out. These conditions insured that "only the best people" were suited for analysis. As Freud put it, "It is gratifying that precisely the most valuable and most highly developed persons are best suited for these curative measures." [20]

One of the cases reported at length lasted seven years. This was the case of the Russian nobleman, a case which Freud called *crucial,* for it was a combination of a childhood and an adult neurosis, one occurring after another with an interval of years between. The report deals only with the childhood neurosis as analyzed when the patient was twenty-four years old. We cannot, here, follow the course of the analysis. We can only note that its crisis centered around the construction of the infantile primal scene which, according to Freud, took place at the age of one and one-half and consisted in seeing his mother and father in the act of coitus. Here, of course, there could be no question of conscious memory, but rather of reconstructing the scene out of the dream material of a later date. The crucial dream took place at the age of four, and was, Freud maintained, determined in its content by the unconscious memory of the primal scene.

The key to the analysis is to be found in Freud's construction or "reconstruction" of the "primal scene." Before discussing the specific nature of the scene, he says "I have now reached the point at which I must abandon the support I have hitherto had from the course of the analysis. I am afraid it will, also be the point at which the reader's belief will abandon me." With this apologetic introduction he announces that the primal scene viewed by the one and one-half year old infant boy, consists in "the picture of a coitus between his parents." But this is not just any coitus but "a coitus in circumstances which were not entirely usual and were especially favorable for observation." The infant witnessed "a coitus à tergo . . . the man upright and the woman bent down like an animal" . . . in this posture "he was able to see his mother's genitals as well as his father's member." By means of this observation the infant sees that his mother has been castrated and concludes that castration is somehow the penalty for Oedipal love and also for masturbation. It is this primal scene which lies at the root of neurotic repression.

This construction of the pirmal scene is crucial because in it all the threads of the analysis are tied together into the psychical mechanism of the neurosis. Of one of the more important of these threads, Freud says: "At this point the boy had to fit himself into a phylogenetic schema, and he did so, although his personal experiences may not have agreed with it. The threats or hints of castration which he had come across had, on the contrary, emanated from women, but this could not hold up the final results for long. In spite of everything it was his father from whom in the end he came to fear castration. In this respect heredity triumphed over accidental experience; in man's prehistory it was unquestionably the father who practiced castration as a punishment and who later softened it down into circumcision."

A question immediately poses itself. Is it the child who has to fit himself into an hereditary racial schema? Or is it Freud who has to fit the boy's mind into a preconceived mold? On this point, Freud says, "It is true that we cannot dispense with the assumption that the child observed a coitus, the sight of which gave him a conviction that castration might be more than an empty threat." [21] But he adds that there are two pillars on which this — and other similar assumptions — rest: On the one hand, the interpretation of dreams, unconscious associations and phantasies by means of the art of symbol translation; and, on the other, the theory of the archaic mental inheritance from man's prehistory. As we have had occasion previously to note, both of these doctrines are borrowed from the cast-off dregs of human intellectual history. That dreams have meaning and that there are such things as innate, hereditary ideas, are superstitions rejected centuries ago when man emerged from the darkness of the fuedal past. And yet they are resurrected by Freud and installed as pillars of psychoanalysis. The possibility of dredging them up was furnished primarily by the contemporary lack of knowledge of the functioning of the higher parts of the brain.

The interpretation of dreams is the *method,* while the phylogenetic inherited mental schema is the final product of that method.

By 1918, the year in which the case of the Russian nobleman was reported, Freud was no longer concerned with defending his method of dream interpretation. It was by then taken for granted. He was, however, still on the defensive with regard to the phylogenetically inherited mental schema—infantile sexuality and the Oedipus complex—and the assumption of hereditary instinctive knowledge.

At the close of his final full length case history, he says that two problems remain. "The first relates to the phylogenetically inherited schemata, which, like the categories of philosophy, are concerned with the business of 'placing' the impressions derived from actual experience." Of the schemata, he ·ays, "I am inclined to take the view that they are precipitates from the history of human civilization. The Oedipus complex, which comprises a child's relation to its parents, is one of them—is, in fact, the best known member of the class. Wherever experiences fail to fit in with the hereditary schema, they become remodelled in the imagination. . . . It is precisely such cases that are calculated to convince us of the independent existence of the schema. We are often able to see the schema triumphing over the experience of the individual."

The second problem discussed by Freud at the conclusion of the case of the Russian nobleman is concerned also with "the hereditary, phylogenetically acquired factor in mental life." It is closely related to the first, "but it is incomparably more important," he says. It will be noted that in the following statement the solution to the problem is set in hypothetical terms. In fact, however, it comprises the heart of the philosophy of psychoanalysis and lies at the center of the *system,* and therefore is a basal assumption. The statement is, indeed, as good a general summary of psychoanalysis as a way of looking at things as can be found anywhere in Freud's writings. "If one considers the behavior of the four-year-old child towards the reactivated primal scene, or even if one thinks of the far simpler reactions of the one-and-a-half-year-old child when the scene was actually experienced, it is hard to dismiss the view that some sort of hardly definable knowledge, something as it were preparatory to an understanding, was at work in the child at the time. What this may have consisted in we can form no conception; we have nothing at our disposal but the single analogy—and it is an excellent one—of the far-reaching *instinctive* knowledge of animals." And he goes on to place this analogy at the basis of his entire system, as a foundation-stone. "If human beings too possessed an instinctive endowment such as this, it would not be surprising that it should be very particularly concerned with the processes of sexual life, even though it could not be by any means confined to them. This instinctive factor would then be the nucleus of the Unconscious, a primitive kind of mental activity, which would later be dethroned and overlaid by human reason, when that faculty came to be acquired, but which in some people, perhaps in everyone, would retain the power of drawing down to it the higher mental processes. Regression would be the return to this instinctive stage, and man would thus be paying for his great new acquisition with his liability to neurosis, and would be bearing witness by the possibility of the neuroses to the existence of those earlier, instinct-like, preliminary stages." [22]

It will be noted that there is no special section devoted to Freud's therapy. In psychoanalysis, the therapy *is* the analysis itself, the theory being that when all the gaps in memory and all the amnesias of the infantile period have been recalled or reconstructed, the mechanism of the illness together with the symptoms will disappear. This follows from the purely mental approach. Since the cause of the illness is said to be the repressed instinctive phases of infantile life together with unconscious memories based on them, it follows that by admitting the unconscious repressed material to consciousness the patient dissipates the causal mechanism of the disease.

Freud says that "the transformation of this unconscious material in the mind of the patient into conscious material must have the result of correcting his deviation from normality and of lifting the compulsion to which his mind has been subjected." Elsewhere he says that "the task of the cure is to remove the amnesias. When all the gaps in memory have been filled in, all the enigmatic products of mental life elucidated, the continuance and even the renewal of the morbid condition is impossible." [23]

According to his own testimony Freud had a considerable number of successful and partially successful analyses—and a fair share of failures. In view of the fact that most of the analyses extended over long periods of time, up to seven or eight years, there could never be certainty in ascertaining the true cause of success. As Freud said of his earlier seduction cases in which he had claimed to have been highly successful, there is always "the possibility of explaining my partial successes in other, familiar ways." [24]

The seven-year analysis of the Russian nobleman, for example, was interrupted by the First World War. After the war, he returned to Freud and was pronounced in good mental health. It seems that the war and the Russian Revolution stripped him of his several hereditary estates—"robbed him of his home, his possessions, and all his family relationship," as Freud put it—and that for the first time in his life he had had to work for a living. What constituted the cure, the analysis or the radically altered circumstances? Freud's answer is, "It may be that his very misery, by gratifying his sense of guilt, contributed to the consolidation of his recovery." Freud cannot lose. Anything can be twisted into a defense of analysis. Not the changed conditions themselves, but their gratification of his hereditary phylogenetic guilt for all the innate, instinctive, degenerate "crimes" of his infancy, was the alleged cause of the cure.

Psychoanalysis as a whole has a built-in defense mechanism. Anyone who criticizes it, or refuses to accept its teaching is himself subjected to analysis. At the turn of the century, during the early years, Freud and his system were attacked on all sides. "The situation obeyed a simple formula," Freud wrote, "men in the mass behaved to psychoanalysis in precisely the same way as individual neurotics under treatment for their disorders." And he added that "it was no small thing to have the whole human race as one's patient." He analyzed this outraged, negative reaction of the human race to his theories, and was gratified and consoled with the thought that "after all everything was taking place as the premises laid down by psychoanalysis declared that it was bound to." Since every individual had, according to him, passed through the purgatory of infantile sexuality and then had promptly at the age of three or four repressed the memory of the entire period into The Unconscious, he concluded that "they were infuriated when psychoanalysis tried to lift the veil of amnesia from their years of childhood. There was only one way out: what psychoanalysis asserted must be false and what posed as a new science must be a tissue of fancies and distortions."[25] Thus any repudiation of Freud's theories is analyzed as a refusal to recognize the infantile repressed material. "To adults," Freud says, "their pre-history seems so inglorious that they refuse to allow themselves to be reminded of it." Resistance to psychoanalysis is *resistance* to The Unconscious—such is the "impregnable" wall constructed around Freud's system.

Chapter XI

PAVLOV'S APPROACH TO MENTAL ILLNESS

PSYCHIATRY, AFTER hundreds of years of collection, classification and collation of disturbed mental phenomena, had finally brought those forms of mental illness due to organic lesions of the brain to the *anatomical* laboratory. As a result, considerable progress had been made in discovering the causes of the so-called *organic* mental diseases. But, as we have previously noted, that branch of psychiatry dealing with the so-called *functional* forms of mental illness, had remained fixed in the stage of *observation*. A tremendous amount of descriptive material had been classified and collated, and systematized into the syndromes of various functional disorders, such as schizophrenia, hysteria, paranoia, neurasthenia, and others. But in the absence of experimental investigation, the work of discovering the interconnections and causal mechanisms of these pathological phenomena was largely speculative. The result was a multitude of "schools," each espousing its own individual systematized guesswork, with a minimum of mutual agreement and a maximum of antagonistic partisanship.

It was within the context of such a contradictory situation in psychiatry that Pavlov carried on his work of inducing pathological psychic phenomena in the laboratory, and determining experimentally at least some of the disordered cerebral interconnections and mechanisms underlying the symptoms of functional mental illness. The psychiatric situation was contradictory since, on the one hand, the physiologist could draw heavily and advantageously on the observed, described, classified and collated phenomena amassed by functional psychiatry, while on the other, he had resolutely and forthrightly to reject most of the theoretical guesswork about the interconnections and causal mechanisms of those symptoms and syndromes. The *observations* were absolutely indispensable—for example those of Kraeplin—while the various *interpretations* of them were by and large best dispensed with.

Pavlov's insistence on the fact that disordered subjective phenomena take place on the basis of pathological states of the brain is directly in the main current of cerebral physiological and pathophysiological tradition and has an impressive line of descent including *all* the illustrious and important figures in the field. The number is legion, but a few names, from many nations, will suffice: F. Goltz, C. E. Beevor, Hughlings Jackson, G. Fritsch, E. Hitzig, David Ferrier, D. Foerster, C. Vogts, O. Vogts, W. B. Cannon, C. Ludwig, J. Müller, S. P. Botkin, I. M. Sechenov, M. Schiff, L. Bianchi, L. Luciano, A. W. Campbell, J. F. Fulton, V. Horsley, H. Nothnagel and A. Cerevkov.

Pavlov's Pathophysiological Investigation of Some Neurotic Symptoms

Speaking of the fusion of mental with cerebral activity, of the objective with the subjective, Pavlov writes, "Naturally, the possibilities for this fusion are provided most of all by cases of disorder of the human brain when distortion of the human subjective world is linked, obviously, with anatomical and physiological disturbances of the higher part of the brain."[1] For thirty-five years he investigated, in addition to the normal physiology of the cerebral hemispheres of dogs, certain pathophysiological states produced in the laboratory. He called these states *experimental neuroses*.*

From 1918 on, he visited neurological and psychiatric clinics with a double purpose in mind. On the one hand, he applied his laboratory findings on experimental neuroses to the interpretation of symptoms observed in the clinics. On the other hand, his clinical observations set new tasks for his laboratory work. In the final years of his life, 1929-36, a close and systematic

*Here we give only the most essential features of Pavlov's work on experimental neuroses, since an extended discussion of the subject is included in *Pavlov and Freud*, Vol. I.

working relationship was established between the laboratory and the clinics.

In his clinical observations, Pavlov's approach differed essentially from the usual one of either the neurologist or the psychiatrist. In the first place, he observed the *objective symptoms* of the patients rather than the *subjective content* of their ideational or emotional states as expressed in words. In the second place, he reasoned physiologically, on the basis of his experimental work, about the causal mechanisms and interconnections of the various objective symptoms. For example, in discussing two clinical cases, Pavlov concludes, on the basis of a number of detailed symptoms, that the most striking features are "the strongly pronounced motor symptoms which are observed in both cases—the catalepsy of the first patient and the tonic reflexes of the second." And he immediately asks himself, "When do these symptoms manifest themselves in animals?" He answers by citing experiments investigating the stages of falling asleep and of awakening in which the second stage, a form of partial sleep or hypnosis, is described as follows: "The motor region of the cortex was already embraced by sleep inhibition while all other parts of the cerebral hemispheres still functioned quite satisfactorily." This normal physiological stage of partial sleep or hypnosis was found in certain cases of experimental neuroses, not as a transient stage quickly passing into other stages of sleep and hypnosis, but as a fixated state lasting days, weeks, months or even years, until the course of nature cured it or until therapeuatic measures were taken to overcome it. Pavlov viewed this "frozen" state of partial sleep involving only the motor area of the cortex as a cerebral mechanism of cataleptic and tonic reflex symptoms. He called this particular pathological mechanism "a fully isolated inhibition of the motor area of the cerebral cortex" and classified it as a form of pathological inertness of isolated areas of the cortex.

The psychiatrists attending the two patients observed by Pavlov saw in these cases a state of stupor evoked by strong emotions. Their inclination was to try to discover what strong emotions arising out of what personal situations had caused the "stupor," and then to try to trace the etiology of their respective conditions and so perhaps dissipate them. Of such a psychoanalytic and psychotherapeutic approach, Pavlov says, "But in the first place, this concerns the cause of the symptoms and not their mechanism."[2] He always maintained that it was the pathophysiological mechanism of the neurosis which had to be discovered and then, on the basis of this exact knowledge the mechanism had to be treated so as to restore normal physiological functioning.

Without exact knowledge of the mechanism, discoverable solely by experimentation and never by observation alone, the psychiatrist, like doctors generally, can only proceed *practically,* or *Pragmatically,* in the use of various therapeutic methods. In functional illness the cause is not, as it is in organic illness, poisons, bacteria and other micro-organisms, injury from blows, etc. It is a disturbance of normal functioning in which the mechanism of the disorder is the primary, immediate cause. What brings about the pathological state of the physiological process is the ultimate cause. The latter may be anything from a general run-down, exhausted condition, due perhaps to somatic illness or over-work, to emotional or intellectual stresses, strains or conflicts. Knowledge of these ultimate causes is important to aid in diagnosis, but primarily for purposes of hygiene—either to prevent functional mental illness in the first place, or to prevent the recurrence of a neurosis after it has once been removed.

Psychoanalysis and psychotherapy tend to mistake ultimate causes for immediate ones, and then to proceed to base analysis and therapy on the ultimate cause rather than on the immediate pathophysiological mechanism underlying and producing the symptoms. As Pavlov said, there may be many ultimate causes of functional mental illness, and to discover them is a very lengthy and complicated task — and for the most part an irrelevant task for *curative* functional medicine. It is a highly relevant task, however, for the science of hygiene. The two together comprise what Pavlov calls "the medicine of the future, i.e., hygiene in the broad sense of the word."[3]

Pavlov's approach is to discover the pathophysiological cerebral mechanism indicated by the complex of symptoms, through a combination of experimental laboratory investigations and systematic clinical observation. After several years of this combined laboratory and clinical work, Pavlov in 1934 concluded that there are certain types of neuroses which can be reproduced experimentally in the form of rough working models, while there are other types which are peculiar to human beings and cannot be experimentally reproduced, even roughly. In general, those neuroses classified as cases of neurasthenia or nervous breakdown, and which are more appropriately treated in the neurological than in the psychiatric clinic, can be, as he put it, "understood and connected with our pathophysiological laboratory facts. . . . Neurasthenic states of different kinds can be fully reproduced in animals." [4]

The special human neuroses, on the contrary—those involving the correlation of the three systems of higher nervous activity, including the specifically human speech system—cannot be reproduced in the laboratory. These latter, for example hysteria and what Pavlov called psychasthenia, involve the dissociation of the three systems and this fact precludes their reproduction in cerebral hemispheres limited to two functional systems. However, while the strictly human neuroses cannot be reproduced as a whole, nevertheless, according to Pavlov, the mechanisms of individual symptoms comprising the total syndrome can be *elucidated* by laboratory facts, and in this manner even these neuroses are subject to pathophysiological investemos and explanation. We will examine some of Pavlov's explanations of certain characteristically human neuroses.

The first psychiatric illness systematically observed and studied by Pavlov was schizophrenia. In the particular cases concerned (hebephrenia and catatonia) his attention was concentrated, not on the subjective phenomena, but on two sets of symptoms. On the one hand, were symptoms of apathy, torpor, negativism, repetition of words and gestures, rigidity, inactivity and stereotyped movements, and on the other hand were symptoms of playfulness, exaggerated familiarity, aggressive excitation, emotionalism and childish behavior in general. With regard to the first set, he analyzed each symptom as the expression of one or another of the hypnotic phases which had, under the influence of morbific agents—the stresses and strains of life—become pathologically frozen or fixed. For example, the symptoms of apathy and torpor were usually ascertained by the failure of a patient to react to questions addressed to him. Pavlov found that if the questions were asked, not in the usual tone or inflection, but very softly and gently, the patient usually responded. This, he maintained, was characteristic of the paradoxical phase of partial sleep, inhibition or hypnosis. The negativism exhibited by some patients, he accounted for in terms of the ultra-paradoxical phase.* The repetition of words (echolalia) and gestures (echopraxia), rigidity (catatonia) and stereotypy were likewise explained by reference to temporary phenomena common in hypnotism, but which in pathological cases had become more or less permanently fixed.

As arrested and frozen phases of hypnosis, this first set of symptoms was viewed by Pavlov as a form of *protective inhibition*, of which sleep (full inhibition) and hypnosis (partial inhibition) are the two general types. The over-strain or collision of the nervous processes had, according to this theory, brought on an irradiating inhibition which on the one hand served to protect the cortical cells from further over-strain, and therefore from further damage, and on the other hand, constituted the pathological cerebral mechanisms underlying and giving rise to the various symptoms.

The second set of symptoms—playfulness, childishness, etc.—Pavlov viewed as the result of the more advanced stages of protective inhibition. Here the irradiating inhibition has already largely engulfed that part of the cortex concerned with the functioning of the speech system. Due to this, the regulative and organizing role of the speech system is abrogated, as it is in normal sleep, and the sensory and unconditioned systems display more or less chaotic and unregulated activity. The schizophrenic at definite stages and in definite variations of his disease exhibits temporary bursts of chaotic excitation of all the lower centres manifested now in causeless and unusual playfulness and joviality, now in excessive sensibility and tearfulness, now in excessive anger and outbursts of aggression.

From both sets of symptoms and their underlying functional mechanisms, Pavlov concludes that at least some of the schizophrenic symptoms are an expression of a chronic pathological hypnotic state. The reason for the chronic hypnosis of schizo-

*For a discussion of hypnotic phases see *Pavlov and Freud*, Vol. I.

phrenics is, according to Pavlov, a nervous system progressively weakened by the impact of life's difficulties and problems. In such a weakened condition, it may become exhausted from further excessive excitation, and *exhaustion* is one of the chief physiological impulses for the appearance of protective inhibition in the form of sleep or hypnosis.

Chronic pathological hypnosis is irradiating inhibition frozen in different degrees of extensity and intensity. "Consequently," Pavlov says, "this state is, on the one hand, pathology, since it prevents the patient from normal activity, and, on the other hand, according to its mechanism, it is still physiology, a physiological remedy, since it protects the cortical cells from the danger of being destroyed as a result of too heavy work." The pathological mechanism of the illness is at the same time a means of preventing organic damage to the cortical cells involved. It is this feature that is characteristic of *functional* mental illness. As long as there is no organic injury, the illness must, according to Pavlov, be considered functional and entirely curable. Full return to normal must be the goal of at least all those forms of neuroses the mechanism of which involves protective inhibition. "There are reasons to assume," he says, "that as long as the (protective) inhibitory process operates, the cortical cells are not gravely damaged, their full return to normal is still possible, they can recover from excessive exhaustion and their pathological process remains reversible. Using the modern terminology, it is only a functional disease." [5]

From his work in the laboratory and from his observation in the psychiatric clinic, Pavlov was convinced that human neuroses and psychoses could best be understood, diagnosed and treated when the pathophysiological mechanisms underlying and causing the symptoms were known. His work in this field only began at the close of his life and certainly can lay no claim to exhaustive investigation or finalized conclusions. What he in fact left in this connection was a legacy of real problems for further work—and a theory and method for solving them.

His analysis of some of the symptoms of certain forms of schizophrenia are primarily important as sign-posts to guide pathophysiological and medical research. They are in a sense Pavlov's last will and testament. Above all they express a conclusion generalized from his own thirty-five years of experimental work on the functioning and malfunctioning of the cerebral hemispheres: That psychic activity is synonymous with higher nervous activity and that, as a corollary, any functional derangement of psychic activity is a functional derangement of higher nervous activity.

As Pavlov would have been the first to admit, no amount of observation in the psychiatric clinic could ever possibly establish his hypothesis. Only the broad and systematic teamwork on a large scale of psychiatric hospital staffs, psychiatric research centers and pathophysiological laboratories could carry forward the concrete investigations necessary to establish the position once and for all, in and through actual case analyses, diagnoses and treatments.

Such a vast program based on Pavlov's approach has been initiated in the Soviet Union. Some of the results of this truly colossal undertaking are already available, and are impressive.* But it is still in the initial stages and the scientific world awaits the outcome of this experiment on a grand scale to determine the validity of Pavlov's physiological principles when applied on the one hand to psychology, child development and education, and on the other to psychiatry and the whole range of functional mental illnesses and their specific diagnoses and therapies. It is a unique experiment in massively planned theoretical and practical research. The outcome *could be* momentous for the mental health, hygiene, education and self-knowledge of mankind.

Confrontation

The immediate confrontation of the two approaches to functional mental illness presents a striking contrast.

While Pavlov's approach brings neuroses back into the realm of pathophysiological and medical science, Freud puts them beyond the pale of science and medicine. In fact, he reenstates the medieval demonological theory of mental illness in

---

*A report on the proceedings of a scientific congress which set this aim was published in English under the title: *Scientific Session on the Physiological Teachings of Academiciam I. P. Pavlov*, Moscow, 1951. For a summary of this and other material see Pavlov and Freud, Vol. I.

which possession by evil spirits is made to account for what now would be called neurotic and psychotic symptoms. The only essential difference is that Freud makes the evil spirits internal rather than external agents. The Freudian evil spirits are evil wishes originating not with the devil but with the dream-constructed degeneracy of infantile sexual impulses, inherited from the myth-constructed pre-history of the human race. Possession by a demon, possession by an unconscious wish, the only real difference is the language.

Freud was fully aware of the close relationship between his theory and that of medieval demonology, and of what was required to make the latter acceptable today. "All that would have been required," he says, "was to replace the religious terminology of those dark and superstitious times by the scientific one of today." [6] Freud wrote this in 1893, before the full flowering of psychoanalysis. But in 1923 he returned to the subject, not in terms of what *could* be done, but what was already accomplished. "Despite the somatic ideology of the era of 'exact' science, the demonological theory of those dark ages has in the long run justified itself. Cases of demonological possession correspond to the neuroses of the present day; in order to understand these latter we have once more had recourse to the conception of psychic forces. What in those days were thought to be evil spirits, to us are base and evil wishes, the derivation of impulses which have been rejected and repressed." He adds, however, one qualification, "In one respect only do we not subscribe to the explanation of these phenomena current in medieval times; we have abandoned the projection of them into the outer world, attributing their origin instead to the inner life of the patient in whom they manifest themselves." [7]

The key point here is the attribution of neurotic states to "psychical forces," whether they be external demons or internal wishes. Freud preserves the content but alters the form of the superstitious demon theory. In doing so he in effect annuls the hard-won progress of medical science and particularly psychiatry. The basic principle of the latter, that mental illness is a disorder of the brain, is a fully conscious rejection of all demon-psychic-force theories, and marks the origin of a scientific approach to the subject—a great victory for man over the forces of darkness and supersition, a battle and a victory which had to be fought and won by each and every branch of science down the centuries.

The medieval demonological theory was the product of human ignorance, at a time when modern medical science was as yet non-existent. Freud, on the other hand, was himself a highly trained scientist. He had been exposed to all the knowledge available in Europe. He studied under leading scientists in Vienna, Berlin and Paris. He knew, and even, in his early years, contributed to, the growing body of knowledge of the human nervous system and its apex, the brain. And yet when confronted with a temporary gap in cerebral physiology, concerning the nature of the higher nervous disorders underlying and giving rise to neuroses, he succumbed to the pressures of his office practice and like Faust sold his soul to the devil.

That he knew better, there can be no question. Over and over again, particularly in the formative years of psychoanalysis, he in effect apologized for what he was doing, and himself called it a poor substitute, a stop-gap measure, for cerebral knowledge.

Today, at long last, the Freudian psychoanalytic approach to functional mental illness is facing a rapidly rising challenge. The challenge, at least in our country, comes not so much on the grounds of principle as on practical efficacy. The stubborn fact is that psychonalysis inspite of its claims has been totally incapable of checking, much less of reversing, the fantastically high incidence of functional mental illness in its host nation, the United States. A search is now in progress for other, for *medical* means of treating and preventing neurotic and psychotic disorders.

In this country, psychoanalysis is being weighed on the powerful scales of practicality, and is in the process of being "found wanting." A recent series on psychology in *Life* Magazine poses as its conclusion the current crucial question, "Shadow of future of mental treatment propounds a major question: whether the ills of the mind are treatable, chiefly by psychological therapy, as provided by the psychoanalyst, or are curable by physical means produced in the laboratory."[8] The final article of the *Life series* is entitled "Where Does Psychology Go From

Here?" and the sub-title is, "While Freud is still debated, scientists open new paths in their search for the true nature of mental ills." Much of the work is in the bio-chemical laboratory in search of effective drugs. The so-called miracle, "happiness" drugs, derivations of reserpine and chlorpromazine—thirty-four million prescriptions in 1956, over and above those sold without prescription—have given a tremendous impetus to this search.

Beyond the practical laboratory search carried on largely by the leading pharmaceutical corporations, for "miracle drugs," scientific and theoretical work is being pursued quietly and patiently on at least two levels, the bio-chemistry of normal and pathological mental states and the physiology and pathophysiology of the brain. For example, in the latter fields. Dr. Jose Delgado of the Yale University School of Medicine is conducting important research into the functioning and malfunctioning of various cerebral centers.

There can be little question that in essence Freudian psychoanalysis, together with its limitless number of psychotherapeutical variations has by and large dismally failed its practical mass-test in the United States as an effective cure of functional mental illness. This hard fact has lent added impetus to the search for other and mainly medical means of understanding, diagnosis and treatment. Medically oriented psychiatry appears to be on the verge of gaining a decisive victory over the "psychical-forces" theory, Freud's as well as the many variations of it.

One conclusion to be drawn in the present chapter is that Freud's unconscious, evil-wish, demon theory of neurosis has little in common with science, medicine or psychiatry, that it is in fact anti-scientific and constitutes essentially a road-block in the path of further development.

It is undoubtedly true that almost any form of medically-oriented psychiatry, when set in immediate opposition to Freud's approach, would prove sufficient, by contrast, to expose the psychoanalytical view of neuroses. The confrontation by Pavlov, however, has the signal advantage of laying bare the prime historical condition for the genesis of such psychical-force theories—namely, the absence of a physiology and pathophysiology of the cerebral hemispheres as a whole. By at least laying a basis for filling the gap in cerebral physiology, the science of higher nervous activity removes the *reason-for-existence* of any purely mental approach.

A further conclusion to be drawn in this chapter is that the science of higher nervous activity, founded by Pavlov, is an effective means of exposing the Freudian theory of neurosis. It not only furnishes a scientific contrast to the speculations and assumptions, the dream interpretations and constructs of psychoanalysis, but it also gives an account of the very phenomena utilized by Freud. It shows how it was possible for Freud to seize hold of certain facts—of dreams and neurotic symptoms—and, with no adequate physiological knowledge to contradict him, to build an entire psychical edifice on their basis. It shows that Freud started from phenomenal *appearances,* and this gives his theories their semblance of credibility.

This is in fact the earmark of speculative, metaphysical theories. They do not spin their tales out of whole cloth, but rather utilize appearances which as yet cannot be accounted for by science. Critics may reject the theories and criticize them and hold them up to scorn and derision. But as long as science is not able to give an alternative, factual, experimentally derived explanation of the phenomena, the theories can thrive on social ignorance. This was true of astrology and alchemy, the forerunning substitutes for astronomy and chemistry. And it was true of the medieval demonological theory of mental illness and of its modern counterpart or revival, the psychoanalytical theory of neuroses. Only the advent of the sciences of astronomy, chemistry and higher nervous activity could finally dispose of the speculative, mystical substitutes. Only patiently, carefully and slowly acquired knowledge serves to rout those impatient, careless and rapidly formed theories which would *leap* the gaps in human understanding of the world, and of man himself.

To accomplish this task of exposing and interring impatient, "leaping" theories, based on appearances and conjectured explanations, it is historically proven that the counterposed science need by no means be a finished product. Astronomy and chemistry are still today incomplete and yet astrology and alchemy have long been dead—or at least have been driven into the backwash of miniscule cults. The science of higher nervous activity, the physiology and pathophysiology of the cerebral hemispheres is already sufficiently developed to lay the ghost of any and all psychic-force theories of functional mental illness. The latter cannot much longer cling to their former priviliged position. Ignorance was their pre-condition, and that ignorance is giving way to the relentless on-march of science.

The catalytic agent in this process is the fearful incidence of mental disorders. The crucible of practical exigency is forcing the issue. Freud has had his mass-test in the United States—and failed. Pavlov is only now undergoing his test on a massive scale in the Soviet Union and elsewhere in the world. In the meantime medically-oriented psychiatry in the United States is in the process of by-passing Freud and his followers, and the various deviations from and variations of his approach. It is a time of great and relatively rapid change in the field of psychiatry. The hey-day of make-shift substitutes is almost at an end—the outcome of that ultimately invincible combination of scientific theory and practical experience.

Chapter XII

PAVLOV AND FREUD

THE TASK OF examining and comparing the life and work of Pavlov and of Freud is now complete. It was said at the outset that the importance of the undertaking derives from the fact that there has been a growing polarization, on a world scale, of psychological and psychiatric thought around these two giant figures during the past half century.

In the course of the two volumes a considerable number of specific evaluations, more or less tentative, have been made. We are now in a position to unite the diverse conclusions. They comprise three levels of investigation: (1) an evaluation of Freud in terms of his own work; (2) an evaluation of Freud by comparison with *any* objective approach, and (3) an evaluation of Freud confronted by Pavlov.

In addition we will make a comparison between the lives, the philosophies and the historical significance of the two men, together with a judgment with regard to the relation of each to the future of psychology and of psychiatry.

An Evaluation of Freud in Terms of His Own Work

At the close of the first chapter it was said that a key problem with regard to an evaluation of Freud in terms of his own work is to determine whether or not his metapsychological speculation, what we have called his myth-making, is an integral part of his working theories. We have examined many of these theories, said to be based mainly on observation of patients, and in each case have found that they explicitly rely on the metapsychological assumptions. As a matter of fact, we found that the very "observations" themselves were determined by the concept of the hereditary mental apparatus, especially by the assumption of an innate archaic language of the unconscious in the form of stereotyped symbols biologically inherited from primitive man. The fact that Freud's "observations" of dreams and the like are seen through the colored glasses of inborn sexual symbolism, transforms these "observations" into *interpretations*. In his theory of repression, of dreams, of character formation and of the etiology of the neuroses, the "observations" have already passed through a dye process indelibly imbuing them with speculative, mythical hues. If this is true of the observations, the raw material of the theories, it is all the more true of the theories themselves.

The working theories, we conclude, cannot be surgically disengaged from the speculative metapsychology. The archaic myths are an inherent and inseparable, homogenized ingredient. Freud-the-investigating-analyst cannot be divorced from Freud-the-maker-of-myths. This fact, substantiated throughout our examination of psychoanalysis, casts a shadow over all the contributions generally credited to Freud even by many who are not to be counted among his followers.

It is widely granted, for example, that Freud made a real contribution toward the liberation of sex from hypocritical puritanism. In this early twentieth century movement there were of course many factors at work, among them: The growth of industrialization and the concentration of population in metropolitan centers; the decline of religion and churches as the hub of social life; the automobile with its release from chaperonage; birth control and the feminist movement; and the rise of the mass media, particularly the movies and radio. Such developments taken together in their cumulative effect, brought about rapid and far-reaching changes in private and social living, patterns of behavior and modes of thought, including profound changes in the attitude toward sex. These latter changes were both reflected and given guidance by such writers on sexual matters as Havelock Ellis and Bertrand Russell. There is no question that Freud also played a part in this development. There is however a serious question about the kind of contribution he made. His sexual theories were not so much concerned with normal sex-life and attitudes as they were with aberrations and perversions. There is a real question whether the latter did not serve more to *misguide* the new movement rather than to give it a healthy, normal direction. From the infantile phases of oral cannibalism and anal sadism to incestuous mother and father love, and from the guilt and castration complexes to penis-envy and the death-wish, Freud led the newly liberated mind through an underworld labyrinth which was held to be biologically inherited from pre-history and inevitably enmeshing each and every individual life. Could such an approach have made an important positive contribution to the liberation of sex from puritanical hypocracy?

It is often maintained also that Freud made real contributions to the understanding of child development and character formation, and therefore to education. Here again, however, the same holds true as with his alleged part in sexual liberation. Did his myth-permeated theories of infantile sexuality and the repression and sublimation of the aberrational phases help parents and teachers to understand and guide the child along healthy and normal lines of development? A definitive answer must wait on investigation of the effect of psychoanalysis on the fields of child development and education. But it is difficult to believe that, for example, the concept of "the anal character" could play a positive part in the progressive changes in education brought about in the past fifty years.

It is likewise widely maintained that, granting the fantastic nature of his theories generally, Freud nevertheless made a genuine contribution to the understanding of the etiology of the neuroses. But since he viewed etiology primarily as a sexual phenomenon, and since his theory of sex was permeated with myths of the innate archaic heritage, mystical psychic-libidinal energy and perverted incestuous sexual and death wishes, the psychoanalytical theory of etiology cannot help but be itself mythical and unscientific, and therefore suspect. There can be little question about the role of sexual life among other factors in the etiology of neuroses. But that it is either the dominant or exclusive determinant has been generally rejected by responsible psychiatry and psychotherapy. The main point, however, concerns not the degree to which sex-life affects etiology but the fact that Freud put the successful or unsuccessful repression and sublimation of innate *perverted* sexual phases at the center of his theory. Such a theory is not simply an over-estimation of the role of sex, but far more importantly a fundamental distortion of it. Can such a view constitute a genuine contribution?

All these "contributions," granted by many non-Freudians and even by anti-Freudians, are posited on the premise that the obviously incredible myths can be discarded while saving the pure alloy of Freud's observations. The contention here is that any such mechanical attempt completely disregards the organic character of psychonanalysis in which the archaic myths are an absolutely indispensable element, one might say the *sine qua non* of all Freud's observations as well as his theories.

Finally there is almost universal agreement that Freud displayed what is called "great humanity." If by this it is meant that he tried to alleviate human suffering and that he played a part in taking seriously a form of illness which had all too frequently been scoffed at as simple malingering, then there is no disagreement. But even here the humanity tends to be poisoned by the distortions of the human mind as irrational and anti-intellectual and as an underworld of perverted drives, phases and mental constructs. He in effect takes the humanity out of man. In this sense it is difficult not to be more deeply impressed by Freud's objective inhumanity rather than by his subjectively human interest.

Our conclusion with regard to the inherent value of Freud's *psychoanalysis* is based primarily on the following essential features of his system, each of which has been investigated and discussed at considerable length in the various sections and chapters of the present volume.

First, *his general approach is purely mental.* Paying lip-service to the established fact that mind is a function of the brain, and particularly of the cerebral hemispheres, he proceeds as if the human psyche were an independent, disembodied phenomenon. Technically, this approach is called *dualistic idealism* in the psychological form of psychophysical parallelism.

Second, *his conceptual material is in large part drawn from the by-ways of human intellectual history.* He explicitly reserved the right, exercised more often than not, to select those ideas and theories which suited his purpose or need: Technically this should be termed *expedient eclecticism*.

Third, his method of observation is unconscious-mind-probing by means primarily of stereotyped symbol-translation of the imagery of dreams, fantasies, slips-of-tongue and pen, symptomatic actions, unconscious associations and neurotic symptoms. By this "empirical" method, in the first place practiced on himself, he collected the "observational material" out of which his theories were constructed. Technically, this method should be called *esoteric introspection*.

Fourth, his all-but-exclusive concern with *the translation of alleged unconscious symbols into sexual meanings* led to the amassing of "observed sexual material" out of which his theories were constructed. Technically, this should be called *interpretive pan-sexualism*.

Fifth, his theory of *the unconscious mind is packed with the inborn mental traits* required to account for the pan-sexual material produced by sexual-symbol-translation. Technically, this should be termed a *revival of the Platonic and medieval doctrine of innate ideas*.

Sixth, his theory of repression is required as the dynamo of mental activity. Its central doctrine is the concept of "psychic energy," based on an analogy with physical and chemical energy. Technically, the theory of repression is a product of *reasoning-by-analogy with the physical-chemical principle of the explosive potential of compressed molecular energy*. It is the impermissible projection of a physical law into an assumed purely mental construct.

Seventh, his theory of the *return of the repressed innate mental tendencies, retaining their full charge of psychic energy,* is at one and the same time the end and the beginning of his psychoanalytical system. The return of the repressed infantile sexual schemata is found in dreams, fantasies, slips of tongue and pen, jokes, unconscious associations and neurotic symptoms. But it was the presumed symbolic imagery of these very phenomena which when translated led in the first place to the construction of the innate and highly charged mental infantile-sexual schemata. The possibility of translation by means of phylogenetically innate sexual symbolism already implies the existence of the phylogenetically hereditary sexual schemata. Technically this is known as *circular-reasoning* or *the fallacy of begging-the-question,* inadmissible as a rational mode of thought.

Eighth, *his theory of dreams is a specific instance of his theory of the return of the repressed infantile mental schemata and wish-impulses based on them.* In sleep, the theory goes, the censorship is reduced and the repressed wish-impulses can, with the aid of disguised unconscious imagery, gain admittance to consciousness. The interpretation of dreams traces this process backwards. By reading the assumed innate stereotyped, symbolic, sexual language of dreams, the return of the repressed is traced ultimately to the originally posited repressed infantile sexual schemata. Technically, this should be called the resurrection *of the age-old but long-since discredited and discarded superstition that dreams have hidden meaning.*

Ninth, his theory of neurosis is still another instance of his theory of the return of the unconscious repressed infantile sexual schemata and wish-impulses based on them. By reading the assumed phylogenetic symbols in the dreams, fantasies, symptomatic actions, unconscious associations and transferences of the patient, the analyst would trace the wish-impulses and motivations of the neurosis to the originally repressed material, and reconstruct the *primal scene* which is presumed to constitute the infantile trauma. Technically, this should be called the *psychic-force theory of neurosis, a revival of the medieval demonological theory of the possession of the soul by evil spirits.*

Tenth, his *metapsychology* is an admitted conjectural attempt to construct a psychological system. Whether in the form of Cs-Pcs-Ucs or of super-ego, ego and id, this three-system view of the mental apparatus is composed of a pyramid of explicit assumptions. The assumptions are then hypostatized into actual mental "entities," spatially located mental "compartments," and irrepressible mental energies, which in turn are employed to substantiate the operative theories of The Unconscious, instincts, repression and so on. Technically, this is *speculative metaphysics* applied to psychology.

Eleventh, and finally, his theory of the origin and development of the human mind is based on a combination of mythology and discredited and discarded anthropological conjectures, including tales: of the primal horde; of the patriarchal father; of the castration of sons and the incestuous monopoly of the women by the dominant father-husband-brother-son; of the deed of patricide; of the guilt and remorse for the original sin; and of the consequent split of the once pristine primal-horde-mind into Cs-Pcs-Ucs; and of the rise of taboos, morals and eventually civilization and culture as the renunciation and repression of primal horde and tribal instincts, memories and wish-impulses. Included also are such specific myths as the origin of power over fire by repression of the instinct to urinate on it, and of a phylogenetically hereditary, primal language common to all people everywhere. It is this "language" which forms the basis, or the rationale, for the art of translation of the stereotyped symbols of dreams, fantasies, neurotic symptoms and the like. The myths are vitally essential elements in both the "working" theories and in the metapsychological system of psychoanalysis. Without these myths, the interpretation of dreams, the fountainhead of Freud's thought, would be completely meaningless. *His myth-making is not a superstructure erected over his "working" theories, but is an integral, inseparable and absolutely indispensable part of the theories themselves.* Technically, his theory of the origin and development of the human mind should be called a *latter-day revival of the art of mythological story-telling.*

To unite these separate characterizations into one general conclusion, we turn to Freud, himself. He once wrote to a friend and admirer, "You often estimate me too highly. For I am not really a man of science, not an observer, not an experimenter, and not a thinker. I am nothing but by temperament a conquistador—an adventurer if you want to translate the word—with the curiosity, the boldness, and the tenacity that belongs to that type of being. Such people are apt to be treasured if they succeed, if they have really discovered anything; otherwise they are thrown aside. And that is not altogether unjust."[1]

An Evaluation of Freud by Comparison with any Objective Approach to Psychology and Psychotherapy

Here we will make only a very brief comparison, on two levels.

First, if Freud's psychoanalysis were to be confronted by any one of a number of types of rational, socially oriented psychotherapy, the contrast would be at once striking and conclusive. Such is the case in spite of the fact that in most instances psychotherapy proceeds with a purely mental approach, paying only dualistic lip-service to mind as a function of the brain, similar in at least this one respect to Freud. The great difference lies in the fact that a rational psychotherapy views mind, not in a social void, not as determined by internal, hereditary instinctive and archaic schemata, but as socially determined by conditions, time and place. Environment, rather than innate constitution, is viewed as the decisive factor in both mental health and mental illness.

This type of psychotherapy regards the etiology of mild, "ambulatory" neuroses as primarily concerned with the buffetings, pressures and conflicts of life in a sharply contradictory society, one in which there is a tremendous gap between inculcated ideals and experienced actuality. In these conditions, life-experience often produces distorted conceptions and disordered emotional reactions. The aim of the therapy is not to make conscious some unconscious, repressed ontogenetic-phylogenetic memories, but to *re-educate* the disoriented person, helping him to supply solutions to problems which he had not been able to solve by himself. To do this the patient is made to understand, among other things, what life-conditions produced his personal difficulties, and wherein lay his "wrong-turns" in meeting them. It is a kind of individual, tutorial, reorientation course, and one which is, in many walks of life in contemporary America, vitally essential.

For our purposes, we need not and cannot go into the details of this type of psychotherapy. In addition, if we were to proceed any further than its most general feature, we would be in the middle of hotly contested, partisan conflicts and differences over methods of procedure and a whole multitude of other factors.[2]

The stress on the role of the social environment and on the experience of the individual within it, enables rational psychotherapy to reveal in a glaring light the extreme onesidedness of Freud's psychoanalysis, in which the role of the social environment is limited primarily to *triggering* the inborn and racially-fated mental schemata. It is entirely untenable and wholly unscientific to deal with any phenomenon as though it existed in a void. If anything, this is more true of the human mind than of most subjects of investigation. And yet Freud approached the individual mind as though it were independent of environmental conditions and subject in the final analysis primarily to determination by phylogenetically hereditary mental traits.

In the second place, if Freud's psychoanalysis were to be confronted by literally any *objective experimental* approach to psychology, the contrast in method would be sufficiently compelling. Compared with the painstaking techniques of laboratory investigation, in which all measures are taken to eliminate as far as possible the subjective, introspective factor as alien to science, Freud's full reliance not only on introspection but on *dream-introspection* annuls all claims to scientific procedure and validity. Compared also with the stress on the designably repeatable and reproducable nature of experiments, the fact that Freud's analyses are not only unrepeatable but unobservable, and that his conclusions cannot be demonstrated but have to be personally experienced, serves to substantiate this conclusion.

Perhaps these are among the reasons why Freud never had a decisive influence on academic experimental psychology in the United States.

Apart from the findings made by Pavlov, a comparison simply of his methods with those of Freud presents a contrast amounting to an indictment. In this sense, Pavlov's experimental principles and procedures represent the standards of science, including experimental psychology. Of this there surely can be no question. In our immediate juxtaposition and confrontation of the methods of Pavlov and of Freud, we were, in essence, comparing Freud's investigative methodology with that of all science. The conclusion was and is that Freud contravened every principle and every standard of procedure in the code of scientific investigation.

Rational psychotherapy and experimental psychology combine to expose two features of Freud's work which together cast a pall of *incredibility* and *unreliability* over all his observations and theories: One, his failure to view, as all science demands, his subject-matter phenomenon as interconnected with its environment; and two, his total disregard for the methodological code of science. To view mind as an isolated, disconnected and self-contained phenomenon, and to investigate it by methods which are in contravention of all the hard-won, historically established principles and standards of science is, in effect, to investigate a distorted, ephemeral entity by non-scientific means.

The case against psychoanalysis becomes still more conclusive when Freud is confronted by Pavlov.

An Evaluation of Freud Confronted by Pavlov

As we have seen in the text, Pavlov and Freud in their respective work, were confronted by an identical situation; an hiatus in the science of cerebral functioning. Cerebral physiology, in spite of all its rapid progress from the early nineteenth century on, had come to an almost complete halt before the cerebral hemispheres, the specific seat of mental life. The *anatomy* of this highest part of the brain was quite well-known, and the physiological functioning of certain individual centers had been experimentally investigated. But *how* the cerebral cortex could comprise the nervous mechanism of the phenomena of consciousness, memory, learning, thought, imagination and knowledge on the one hand, and on the other, of sleep and dreams, hypnosis and hypnotic suggestion, neurosis and neurotic symptoms, remained an enigma wrapped in mystery.

The contrast in the manner in which the two men met the challenge of this crucial hiatus in human knowledge forms the essential basis for the confrontation and comparison of their work. Freud, in his impatience under the pressure of having to treat his private, ambulatory-neurotic cases, attempted to leap the wide and deep gap with the aid of the vaulting poles of dream interpretation and metaphysical speculation. Pavlov, on the contrary, settled down to a patient and persistent attempt to fill the gap by careful and controlled laboratory experimentation and systematic clinical observation.

Pavlov and Freud, each in his own way, thus tried to dissolve the mystery surrounding mental phenomena. The two attempts touch most closely in the borderline and pathological states. Here there can be, as we have witnessed, an almost precise one-to-one comparison of the work of the two men.

In each instance, the confrontation produces a sharp and

decisive, if not overwhelming contrast. When confronted by the experimentally derived physiological explanation of sleep and dreams, Freud's theories of the withdrawal of libido and return to the foetal state in sleep, and of the return of the repressed instincts and archaic heritage in dreams, appears, indeed, an impoverished, fantasied and mythical substitute for scientific knowledge. When confronted by the physiological explanation of hypnosis and hypnotic suggestion, Freud's theory that the eyes of the hypnotist call forth a return of the repressed, phylogenetically hereditary memory of the primal-horde father which lends its charge of psychic energy to the hypnotist and constitutes his animal-magnetic power over the hypnotee, such a theory appears fantastic in the extreme—so much so that one wonders how, even lacking a physiological explanation, anyone could take it seriously. When confronted by the experimentally and clinically derived pathophysiological explanation of certain of the higher nervous mechanisms underlying neurotic states and symptoms, Freud's theory of the return of the repressed infantile-sexual, phylogenetically hereditary schemata and primal-scene memories, appears not only fantastic, but more seriously as an affront to mankind's hard-won victory over the superstitious theory of evil spirits possessing the mind in sleep, dreams and neuroses.

The confrontation of Freud's specific theories by Pavlov's counter-theories, serves to demonstrate how far Freud had strayed from the path of science. It likewise underscores the fact that there can be no leaping-of-the-gaps in human knowledge, that there is no short-cut, that there is no substitute for the slow-but-sure methods of science—and that the inescapable result of impatience in such matters is myth-making, at a time when there is no need whatever for myths.

Freud accounted by some mythical tale or other for most of the phenomena of mental life. Pavlov, while he undoubtedly laid a basis for the higher nervous explanation of consciousness, thought, memory, imagination, and will, did not live long enough to apply his methods and theories to these phenomena, except in a few illuminating references. Moving from fact to fact, his method was far slower, but by the same token, more reliable.

It is a fact, however, that Freud himself based his psychoanalytical system on the very phenomena for which Pavlov was best able to give experimentally derived explanations. Freud rooted psychoanalysis in the continuing ignorance of the cerebral mechanisms of sleep and dreams, hypnosis and hypnotic suggestion, neurosis and neurotic symptoms. But it was precisely these mechanisms which Pavlov investigated experimentally. It was Freud's bad luck, or ill-fate if you will, to count on the long-range existence of specific forms of ignorance, which at the very time of his myth-making, were being transformed into knowledge. The ancient, legitimate myth-makers could count on hundreds and thousands of years of ignorance and therefore a long life for the products of their vivid imaginations. But the hazards of modern myth-making come high. Freud had actually only a brief decade at the close of the last century—the exact period in which he put together his dream-creation.

The confrontation by Pavlov brings us to a summary conclusion with regard to Freud; that, in spite of scientific aspirations and intentions, he was an impatient and improvident maker-of-myths who tried vainly to leap a temporary hiatus in cerebral physiology, with the result that his psychoanalysis constitutes a momentary phenomenon produced by a situation so transitory that it began to pass out of existence almost as soon as he had exploited it.

A Comparison of the Lives of Pavlov and Freud

In Volume I of *Pavlov and Freud* we traced the course of Pavlov's life through three periods of scientific activity covering some sixty years: Ten years of experimental investigation of the nervous regulation of blood circulation; fifteen years in the experimental study of nervous regulation of digestion, for which he won the Nobel Prize in 1904; and the remainder of his long life, thirty-five years, in the experimental investigation of higher nervous (psychic) activity. This life-story could be characterized as the tale of the making of an outstanding scientist.

In the present volume, we began by tracing Freud's life through its two distinct phases. We are now in a position to characterize the second phase of his life-story as a tale of the making of a pseudo-scientist. A brief, outline interweaving of these two stories will serve to highlight the respective characterizations.

The lives of the two men, born seven years apart, run on remarkably parallel tracks until around 1886 when Pavlov was thirty-seven and Freud thirty. Prior to 1886, both had studied science and particularly anatomy and physiology at their universities, had won medical degrees, and had worked in laboratories devoted to the investigation of the nervous systems of sub-human forms of life. There had been, however, two significant differences. First, while most of Pavlov's work had been in *experimental* physiology and anatomy, the bulk of Freud's had been in *descriptive* physiology and anatomy carried on by means of careful microscopic *observation*. Second, while Pavlov had moved away from medicine into the science of physiology and had spent ten years on blood circulation, Freud had been forced, by anti-semitism, to move away from physiology into medicine.

Around the year 1886, Pavlov turned to the experimental study of the nervous regulation of digestion, impelled by problems arising in his previous scientific work. At about the same time, Freud turned from his neurological investigations in the clinics of Vienna and Paris to the practical task of treating ambulatory neurotics in his newly established private office. He was impelled to make this further move away from "pure" scientific work toward practical medicine through marriage and the pressing economic necessity of supporting his wife and expected family. On the other hand it should be noted here that Pavlov and his wife were so poor that they were forced to live separately, he in the laboratory and she with relatives, during the early years of his career. This might be called a sacrifice so that the pursuit of "pure" research science could be continued without having to change to the relatively more lucrative work of medical practice.

Following these 1886 moves, the lives of the two men progressively diverge, first to the point of contrast and eventually to the point of absolute contradiction.

In the fifteen years during which Pavlov was carrying on his prize-winning laboratory work on the nervous regulation of digestion and was appointed Professor of Pharmacology at the Military Medical Academy and head of the department of physiology at the Institute of Experimental Medicine, both in St. Petersburg (now Leningrad), Freud was in the lonely throes of constructing psychoanalysis by means of interpreting his own and his patients' dreams, fantasies and neurotic symptoms. He was impelled thus to abandon his long scientific training and principles and to turn to whatever means of treatment he could find, because at the time none of the pertinent sciences—including cerebral physiology, psychiatry, neurology and psychology—could offer him any real clues on how to treat the ambulatory neurotics who came to him for help. Under the pressure of his private practice, Freud turned his back on science and sought out the by-ways and back-alleys, the forbidden and the sensational, the discarded and the repudiated, the offal of human intellectual history, as source material. "Let down" by science he turned to pseudo-science. It is as though an astronomer, frustrated in the solution of a great astro-problem, were to "take it out on" the science that had "failed him" by turning to astrology where all "answers" can be found. Freud turned from physiology and neurology to dream-symbol-reading, perverted sexology, and a spurious social psychology and anthropology.

At the time Pavlov was moving into the experimental examination of the cerebral hemispheres, around the turn of the century, impelled by specific problems which had arisen in his previous work, Freud was publishing what is generally considered to be his *magnum opus, The Interpretation of Dreams.*

From 1900 on, the lives of the two men run in precisely opposite directions and their theories inevitably meet and clash at decisive points. These points, as we indicated in the previous section, are six in number: Sleep and dreams, hypnosis and hypnotic suggestion, neurosis and neurotic symptoms. In the very years, when Freud was elaborating his mythical, purely mental mechanism to account for the six types of psychic activity, Pavlov was laying the *basis* for disclosing, and finally to a significant extent *actually discovering* many of the physiological and pathophysiological cerebral mechanisms underlying these same six phenomena. By accomplishing this feat, Pavlov was, among other ultimately far more important things, cutting the ground from under Freud's speculative constructions at the very time that they were being constructed.

Philosophical, Scientific and Historical Significance

The Freudian rocket was built in Vienna but launched in the United States. Psychoanalysis never gained the broad foothold in other countries that it did in ours. France had its own Pierre Janet; Germany remained largely within the experimental traditions of Helmholtz and Wundt and medically oriented psychiatry; Austria never really took its own to its bosom; and Great Britain and Russia, though subjected to the influence, never succumbed as did the United States. Our country not only launched psychoanalysis, but became its world-center and dissemination point.

Just as a particular transitory set of conditions in cerebral physiology, psychology and psychiatry gave rise to Freud, so a set of ideological and historical conditions in the United States insured his influence.*

It can be said, in the most general terms, that Freud's success in America was in large part due to the fact that his philosophy was entirely consonant with the predominant national outlook. The dualistic, subjective idealism of his approach to the human mind posed little scientific danger to the semi-official ideology. On the contrary, it by and large enhanced that ideology by giving obscurantism a broader base in the mind and culture of the American people.

The exact contrary, of course, was true of Pavlov's philosophy. The consistent and militant monistic materialsm of the science of higher nervous activity was, and is, in the sharpest possible opposition to the prevailing manner of thought. This in itself is sufficient to account for the relatively slow rate of recognition of Pavlov's science. But there was, and is, at least one more powerful influence at work.

For literally thousands of years mankind has been taught to view the human mind or soul as some kind of extraordinary

*For an extended treatment of this subject another book is in preparation.

and miraculous phenomenon requiring an extra-mundane, extra-scientific explanation. This mysterious and mystical approach to mind is deeply imbedded in all of us, and is not easily uprooted.

During the last three thousand years of this tenacious belief, there have been materialist philosophers who have insisted that mind is a natural phenomenon dependent on the body and particularly the brain. With the development of modern science, and particularly with progress in cerebral physiology, nineteenth century materialist philosophers and scientists insisted that mind is a *function* of matter highly organized in the form of the human brain, specifically the cerebral hemispheres. But so long as it was as yet unknown just how the hemispheres could give rise to mental life, the materialist position was almost in the position of a *counter-belief*, in spite of the fact that the inference was inherent in all science. Only when science could *demonstrate* first, that the cerebral hemispheres constitute the specific organ or seat of mind—which was done by the method of extirpation in the 1870's—and second, that there are specific mechanisms of cortical functioning underlying mental activity, only then could materialism be *fully* transformed from a philosophical doctrine into an established *scientific* principle derived from experimentation. This final demonstration that mind is a function of the brain, is the greatest contribution of the science of higher nervous activity. At the same time it is a bitter pill to swallow for it eliminates the last refuge of human exceptionalism to the pervading order of natural law.

Full acceptance of the science of higher nervous activity would entail the transformation not only of psychology and psychiatry into mature sciences, but also eventually of the thinking of each and every human being.

Pavlov went a long way toward taking the mystery out of mind, while Freud in effect deepened and complicated that mystery.

In these terms we can begin to understand the philosophical, scientific and historical significance of the two men.

Philosophically, Freud was an exponent of an anti-scientific subjective idealist world outlook and method; *scientifically*, he was an exponent of speculative, instinct-psychology, perpetuating the myth of the mysterious human mind; *historically,* he tried to leap rather than fill a major gap in human knowledge and therefore can have little bearing on the future of psychology and psychiatry, save as an impediment.

The significance of Pavlov is quite another matter. *Philosophically,* he was not only an exponent of monistic materialism and the scientific method, but in fact made significant contributions which strengthen the outlook and method of science in the unending struggle against ignorance, superstition and pseudo-science, and against their exploitation in reactionary ideology. *Scientifically,* he in essence eliminated the hiatus in cerebral physiology, which in turn puts psychology and functional psychiatry in a position to become fully mature, experimental sciences. The future of psychology will undoubtedly be closely intermeshed with the science of higher nervous activity—and the same holds for functional psychiatry. *Historically,* Pavlov has already won a permanent place of honor in the pantheon of science. As time goes on, he may be recognized the world over as sharing the kind of significance assigned to a Copernicus, a Darwin, a Marx—marking great turning points in human knowledge.

Toward A Scientific Psychology and Psychiatry

The central thesis of the two volumes of *Pavlov and Freud* is that mental life cannot be anything but the functioning of the human nervous system, in the first place the brain. Mental activity *is* higher nervous activity. This, however, does not mean the *reduction* of the mental to the physiological. For cerebral functioning takes place within concrete historical, cultural, social and individual conditions of time and place. Without higher nervous activity there is no mental life. But *what* is thought and felt and expressed in behavioral action does not depend on, or is not determined by, physiological functioning—except in the case of mental illness. The *content* of thought, feeling and action is not a product of cerebral functioning. It is a product of society. The kind of society in which a person lives and the individual manner in which he participates in that society will ultimately determine the character of his thinking, feeling and acting.

Higher nervous activity, however, not only makes thinking, feeling and acting possible. In addition it embodies laws of functioning which govern the *formation* of historically constituted psychic qualities, for example, the manual and mental skills, including the use of tools and the ability to speak, sing, read, write, and work with numbers.

If psychology is the science concerned with discovering how psychic qualities are formed and how they can be developed and changed through education and through alteration of environmental conditions to the end that individuals may lead socially useful and personally satisfying and creative lives, then the corollary is that the science of psychology should be based on knowledge of the facts and laws of higher nervous activity underlying the formation of these qualities. By the same token, a scientific psychology should not limit itself to a knowledge of cerebral physiology. It should base itself on scientific knowledge of society, on the social science of history, political economy and sociology. It should also be based on a scientific epistemology or theory of consciousness, knowledge and truth; one which recognizes the decisiveness of practice as well as the role of theory in the interaction between human beings and their natural and social environment.

The science of higher nervous activity together with the social sciences and scientific epistemology would in this case constitute the three *prerequisites* for the development of a mature, as opposed to a descriptive or a speculative, science of psychology. Historically speaking, psychology has either not had available, or has disregarded, these three prerequisites and therefore down to the present time has tended to present a composite of description and speculation. At its best, in experimental psychology, it has been primarily descriptive with emphasis on statistical data and correlations. At its second best, in behaviorism, gestaltism, functionalism, operationism and so forth, it has been a mixture of experimental description and speculative theory. At its worst, as in Freudian psychoanalysis, it has been almost wholly speculative.

The future of psychology, then, would seem to hinge on the elimination of speculation, in particular the elimination of Freudianism, and on the wedding of experimental psychology with the three prerequisites—cerebral physiology, the social sciences and a scientific epistemology.

While psychology is concerned with the healthy normal functioning of the brain in its interaction with the environment, functional psychiatry is the diagnosis and treatment of cerebral *malfunctioning*. The causes of cerebral malfunctioning can be any overstrain of the nervous cells and processes: Overpowering or conflicting stimuli, emotional strain, mental conflict, and frustration due to unrequited love or social pressure. But whatever the cause, the effect is overstrain of one kind or another resulting in one or another form of higher nervous malfunctioning manifested in confused or disturbed thought, feeling and behavior.

Such an approach to functional mental illness would bring psychiatry wholly back within the fold of medicine. Its basic tenet would then be that mental illness is an illness of the brain and that it can be treated by intervention in the cerebral processes to reverse and eliminate the malfunctionings. Intervention of this kind could be either verbal, psychotherapy or medicinal, drugs, sleep, hypnosis, etc. In either case, it would be intervention in the form of action on the higher nervous activity to restore healthy functioning. To intervene in this manner would require scientific knowledge in the form of a pathophysiology of cerebral processes.

The Pavlovian science of higher nervous activity includes at least the beginnings of a pathophysiology of the higher parts of the brain. But this science cannot of itself give rise to either a scientific functional psychiatry or a scientific psychotherapy. Any claim to the contrary would be simply false. It can, and does however, legitimately claim to be an indispensable *basis* on which both sciences can achieve the status of fully scientific disciplines.

Pathophysiology of the higher nervous activity, it would seem, should form one indispensable prerequisite for the rise of a fully mature and scientific psychiatry. Another such requisite would be the biochemistry of nervous processes and the changes which take place in the transition from healthy to pathological states.

Today both these prerequisites are being developed rapidly,

cerebral pathophysiology primarily in the Soviet Union, cerebral biochemistry in the United States. But not even the two prerequisites together can give rise to a scientific psychiatry. The latter would require, it appears, a marriage of the prerequisites with the descriptive knowledge of functional mental illness developed by the sciences of psychiatry and neurology over the past hundred and fifty years. Such a union could go a long way toward the transformation of psychiatry from a largely descriptive and pragmatic discipline into a mature and exact medical science.

One of the factors standing in the way of such a development is the concept, so entrenched in the modern mind by Freud, that functional mental illness can be dealt with outside the domain of medicine in a purely mental manner. The Freudian speculations and fanciful theories, together with the dream- and symbol-reading methods which they entail, stand as divertissements waylaying the progress of psychiatric science. Thus, if the above is correct, a further condition for the development of a scientific psychiatry is the reduction and final elimination of psychoanalytic influence.

We seem to be entering an age in which at least the foundations are fast being laid for the maturation of psychology and psychiatry. Perhaps at long last man stands at the threshold of realization of his fondest dream, to understand his own mind in health and in illness.

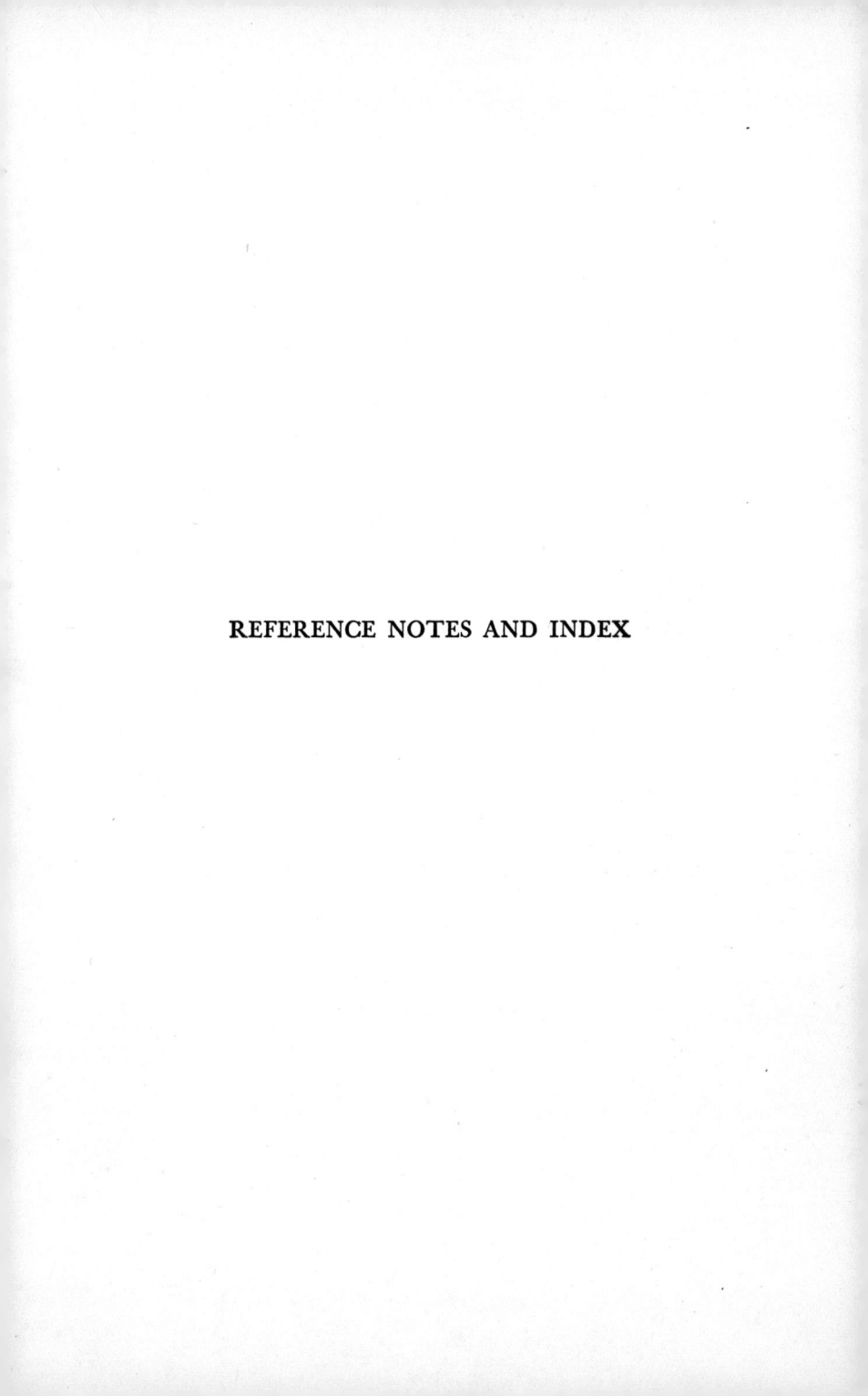

REFERENCE NOTES AND INDEX

REFERENCE NOTES

CHAPTER I

1 Ernest, Jones, *The Life and Works of Sigmund Freud*, Vol. I, New York, 1953, p. 40.
2 *Ibid.*, p. 43.
3 Sigmund Freud, *An Autobiographical Study*, London, 1950, p. 29
4 Sigmund Freud, *The Origin of Psycho-Analysis*, New York, 1954, p. 255.
6 Freud, Letter, 1898. Quoted by Ernest Jones in *The Life and Work of Sigmund Freud*, New York, 1953, p. 395.
7 Freud, *Collected Papers*, Vol. IV, London, 1953, p. 107.
8 Freud, *Gesammelte Werke*, XI, p. 14. Quoted by Jones, *Life and Work of Sigmund Freud*, Vol. I, p. 395.
9 Freud, *An Autobiographical Study*, p. 50.
10 Freud, *Psychopathology of Everyday Life*, London, 1949.
11 Freud, "Wit and Its Relation to the Unconscious," included in *The Basic*
12 Freud, *Beyond the Pleasure Principle*, New York, 1950, p. 37.
13 Freud, *The Ego and the Id*, London, 1950, pp. 27-30.
14 Freud, *Civilization and Its Discontents*, pp. 142-43.
15 Freud, *An Autobiographical Study*, p. 91.
16 Freud, *Collected Papers*, Vol. V, p. 302.
17 Freud, *Moses and Monotheism*, New York, 1949, pp. 207-08.
18 Freud, *Totem and Taboo*, New York, 1952, pp 141-42.
19 Freud, *Totem and Taboo*, pp. 146, 156, 157.
20 Freud, *Moses and Monotheism*, pp. 172-73.
21 Freud, *Collected Papers*, Vol. V, p. 285.
22 *Ibid.*, pp. 280-285.
23 Freud, *Collected Papers*, Vol. V, pp. 196-197.

CHAPTER II

1 Freud, *The Interpretation of Dreams*, p. 215.
2 Pavlov, *Selected Works*, p. 190.
3 *Ibid.*, pp. 193-94.
4 Freud, *Interpretation of Dreams*, pp. 108-11.
5 *Ibid.*, p. 341.
6 Freud, *Introductory Lectures on Psycho-Analysis*, London, 1929, p. 126.
7 *Ibid.*, p. 129.
8 Freud, *Interpretation of Dreams*, p. 341.
9 Freud, *Introductory Lectures on Psycho-Analysis*, pp. 129-32.
10 Freud, *The Interpretation of Dreams*, pp. 341-42.
11 Freud, *Introductory Lectures on Psycho-Analysis*, pp. 14-15, 13.

CHAPTER III

1 Freud, *Collected Papers*, Vol. I, p. 299.
2 Freud, *An Autobiographical Study*, pp. 50-51.
3 Freud, *Collected Papers*, Vol I, p. 298.
4 Freud, *An Autobiographical Study*, pp. 50-53.
5 Freud, *The Interpretation of Dreams*, especially Chapter VII, and *The Collected Papers*, Vol. I.
6 Freud, *Introductory Lectures*, p. 263.
7 Freud, *New Introductory Lectures*, p. 141.
8 Freud, *The Ego and the Id*, pp. 61-62.

CHAPTER IV

1 Freud, *New Introductory Lectures on Psychoanalysis*, New York, 1933, p. 131.
2 Freud, *Beyond the Pleasure Principle*, p. 43.
3 *Ibid.*, p. 69.
4 Freud, *Collected Papers*, Vol. IV, pp. 61, 64.
5 *Ibid.*, pp. 66, 67.
6 Freud, *New Introductory Lectures*, pp. 141, 147. (We here present Freud's final choice and classification of instincts.)
7 Freud, *New Introductory Lectures*, p. 142.
8 Freud, *Civilization and Its Discontents*, pp. 97-98, 102.
9 Freud, *New Introductory Lectures*, p. 142.
10 Pavlov, *Selected Works*, p. 180.
11 *Ibid.*, pp. 180-83.

CHAPTER V

1 Freud, *The Interpretation of Dreams*, p. 495.
2 *Ibid.*, p. 494.
3 Developed primarily in the following books: *The Interpretation of Dreams*, Chapter VII; *Col. Papers*, Vol. IV, pp. 13-172; *Introductory Lectures on Psycho-Analysis*; *Psychopathology of Everyday Life*; *Beyond the Pleasure Principle*.
4 Developed primarily in the following books: *New Introductory Lectures*; *The Ego and the Id*; *Group Psychology*.
5 Freud, *Col. Papers*, Vol. IV, p. 120.
6 *Ibid.*, p. 23.
7 Freud, *The Psychopathology of Everyday Life*.
8 Freud, *Col. Papers*, Vol. IV, pp. 23-24.
9 Freud, *The Interpretation of Dreams*.
10 Freud, *Col. Papers*, Vol. III.
11 Freud, *Collected Papers*, Vol. IV, p. 124.
12 *Ibid.*, p. 23.
13 Freud, *Beyond the Pleasure Principle*, pp. 27-33.
14 Loc. civ.
15 For experimental evidence for fused reflexes see *Pavlov and Freud*, Vol. I, pp. 83-86.
16 Freud, *Beyond the Pleasure Principle*, p. 54.
17 Freud, *Collected Papers*, Vol. IV, p. 34.

REFERENCE NOTES 245

CHAPTER VI

1 Freud, *Collected Papers*, Vol. IV, pp. 23-24.
2 Freud, *Group Psychology and the Analysis of the Ego*, pp. 95-99.
3 *Ibid.*, p. 98.
4 Freud, *Collected Papers*, Vol. IV, pp. 137, 138.
5 Freud, *Beyond the Pleasure Principle*, p. 35.
6 Freud, *Collected Papers*, Vol. IV, p. 139.
7 Pavlov, *Lectures on Conditioned Reflexes*, p. 311.
8 Pavlov, *Selected Works*, p. 386.
9 Pavlov, *Selected Works*, pp. 387-88.

CHAPTER VII

1 Freud, *An Autobiographical Study*, pp. 27-28.
2 Freud, *The Interpretation of Dreams*, pp. 92, 96, 333.
3 *Ibid.*
4 Gustave Le Bon, *Psychologie des Foules*, Paris, 1895. English translation, *The Crowd: A Study of the Popular Mind*, 12th impression, 1920.
5 Le Bon. *The Psychology of Crowds*, quoted by Freud in *Group Psychology*, p. 8.
6 Freud, *Collected Papers*, Vol. V, p. 344.
7 Freud, *Collected Papers*, Vol. II, p. 287.
8 Alfred Weber and Ralph Barton Perry, *History of Philosophy*, New York, 1925, p. 566.
9 Freud, *Collected Papers*, Vol. II, pp. 287-288.
10 For a discussion of these two men and their writings see *Pavlov and Freud*, Vol. I.
11 Paper read before the Vienna Academy in 1870.
12 Even such an otherwise advanced book as Joseph Furst's *The Neurotic* exhibits this feature.
13 For an investigation and evaluation of Thorndike and of behaviorism, see *Pavlov and Freud*, Vol. I.

CHAPTER VIII

1 Freud, *The Question of Lay Analysis*, New York, 1950, p. 29.
2 Freud, *Civilization and Its Discontents*, p. 136.
3 Freud, *Totem and Taboo*, New York, 1939 (Originally published in 1912), pp. 207-08.
4 Freud, *Moses and Monotheism*, pp. 53, 73.
5 Freud, *Totem and Taboo*, p. 141.
6 For this account see principally Freud, *Totem and Taboo*, and *Moses and Monotheism*.
7 Freud, *Totem and Taboo*, p. 141.
8 Freud, *Civilization and Its Discontents*, pp. 50-51.
9 Freud, *Collected Papers*, Vol. V, p. 290.
10 Freud, *New Introductory Lectures*, pp. 104-05.
11 *Ibid.*, p. 108.
12 *Ibid.*, p. 109.
13 Freud, *Collected Papers*, p. 313.
14 Freud, *Moses and Monotheism*, pp. 157-59.

15 Freud, *Collected Works*, Vol. II, pp. 82-83.
16 Freud, *Civilization and its Discontents*, p. 63.
17 Freud, *Introductory Lectures on Psychoanalysis*, p. 300.
18 Freud, *Civilization and Its Discontents*, pp. 141-42.
19 *Collected Papers*, Vol. IV, pp. 103, 301, 314, 300.
20 Freud, *Civilization and Its Discontents*, pp. 63, 123.
21 Freud, *Introductory Lectures on Psychoanalysis*, p. 168.
22 Freud, "Infantile Sexuality," in *Basic Writings*, pp. 597, 598.
23 Freud, *Collected Papers*, Vol. II, "Character and Anal Eroticism," pp. 45-50.
24 *Ibid.*, p. 164.
25 Freud, "Three Contributions to the Theory of Sex," *Basic Works*, p. 617. Here Freud says: "The incest barrier probably belongs to the historical acquisitions of humanity and, like other moral taboos, it must be fixed in many individuals through organic heredity."
Introductory Lectures on Psychoanalysis, p. 278.)
26 Freud, *Group Psychology and the Analysis of the Ego*, p. 61.
27 Freud, *Basic Works*, p. 617.
28 Freud, *Collected Papers*, Vol. II, pp. 269-270.
29 *Ibid.*, pp. 271-76.
30 Freud, *Introductory Lectures*, p. 283.
31 Freud, *Collected Papers*, Vol. V. pp. 190-97.
32 Freud, *Collected Papers*, Vol. V, p. 186.
33 Freud, *Collected Papers*, Vol. II, p. 175.
34 Freud, *Basic Works*, p. 617.

CHAPTER IX

1 Pavlov, *Selected Works*, p. 590.
2 *Ibid.*, p. 569.
3 *Ibid.*, p. 441.
4 *Ibid.*, pp. 553-59.
5 *Ibid.*, p. 583.
6 *Ibid.*, p. 561.
7 *Ibid.*, p. 562.
8 *Ibid.*, p. 567.
9 *Pavlov and Freud*, Vol. I, pp. 87-99.
10 Freud, *An Autobiographical Study*, p. 129.

CHAPTER X

1 Benjamin Rush, *Medical Injuries and Observations upon the Diseases of the Mind*. Philadelphia, 1812, p. 28.
2 Freud, *Collected Papers*, Vol. V, p. 295.
3 Freud, *Collected Papers*, Vol. I, p. 22.
4 *Ibid.*, p. 57.
5 Freud, *Collected Papers*, Vol. V, pp. 295-96.
6 Freud, "Some Points in a Comparative Study of Organic and Hysterical Paralysis," *Archives de Neurologie*, No. 77, 1893.
7 Freud, *Collected Papers*, Vol. V, pp. 53, 55, 57.
8 *Ibid.*, pp. 148-49.
9 *Ibid.*, pp. 185, 268.

10 *Ibid.*, pp. 198, 200, 220, 299.
11 Freud, *An Autobiographical Study*, pp. 60-61.
12 Freud, *Letters: The Origins of Psychoanalysis*, pp. 215 and 218.
13 *Ibid.*, pp. 215-18.
14 *Ibid.*, pp. 210-45.
15 *Ibid.*, p. 234.
16 Freud, *Collected Papers*, Vol. I, pp. 299-300.
17 Freud, *Collected Papers*, Vol. III, pp. 527-28.
18 *Ibid.*, pp. 171-262.
19 *Ibid.*, p. 286.
20 Freud, *Collected Papers*, Vol. I, pp. 245, 257, 259.
21 *Ibid.*, pp. 507-08, 513-15, 565, 531.
22 *Ibid.*, pp. 603-04.
23 Freud, *Collected Papers*, Vol. I, pp. 261, 269.
24 Freud, *Letters: The Origins of Psychoanalysis*, p. 215.
25 Freud, *Collected Papers*, Vol. V, pp. 172-73.

CHAPTER XI

1 Pavlov, *Selected Works*, p. 455.
2 *Ibid.*
3 *Ibid.*, p. 490.
4 *Ibid.*, pp. 468-69.
5 *Ibid.*, pp. 514-15.
6 Freud, *Collected Papers*, Vol. I, p. 20.
7 Freud, *Collected Papers*, Vol. IV, pp. 436-37.
acquisitions of humanity and, like other moral taboos, it must be fixed in
8 *Life*, February 4, 1957.

CHAPTER XII

1 Freud, Letter to Wilhelm Fliess, February 1, 1900. Quoted by Ernest Jones, *The Life and Work of Sigmund Freud*, Vol. I, New York, 1953, p. 384.
2 Perhaps the most advanced example of this type of psychotherapy is to be found in Joseph Furst's *The Neurotic*, New York, 1954.

INDEX

Acinous glands, 13
Adaptation, 64, 65, 67, 159-60, 167, 168
Aggression, 28
Ambivalence, 82, 140
Ambulatory neuroses, 16, 45
Amnesia, 17
Analysis, 64-5, 172
Anna O, case of, 19, 25
Anti-cathexis, 59, 60, 66
Anti-semitism, 13
Art of interpretation, 26, 27, 28
Artemidorus, 114
Asphasia, 15
Association, 91-4, 124, 125, 160, 161-2, 163, 164, 165
Atheism, 11
Attention, 84-5, 90-4

Bain, Alexander, 125
Beevor, C. E., 209
Behaviorism, 69, 130, 161
Bergson, Henri, 121
Bernard, Claude, 127
Bernays, Martha, 13, 16
Bernheim, Hippolyte, 17, 23, 114, 120
Beyond the Pleasure Principle, Freud, 29
Bianchi, L., 209
Binet, Alfred, 182, 184
Bonaparte, Princess Marie, 37
Botkin, S. P., 127, 209
Brener, Joseph, 18, 19, 23, 25, 182, 184
Brill, A. A., 30, 31
Brücke, Ernst, 11, 12, 13, 16
Bruno, 175

Campbell, A. W., 209
Cannon, W. B., 209
Cerevkov, A., 209
Castration, 35, 153, 202
Catharsis, 19, 57
Cathartic method, 23, 25
Cathexis, 56, 57, 58-61, 66
Censor, 55, 66, 136

Cerebral hemispheres, 44, 62, 64, 74, 168, 175
Cerebral physiology, 21
Chain reflex, 75, 76
Charcot, Jean Martin, 14, 15, 18, 24, 180, 181, 182, 183, 184
Civilization and Its Discontents, Freud, 29
Clark University, 31
Claus, Carl, 12
Collective mind, 33
Conditioned reflex, 45; theory of, 61-6; 89-94, 130, 159, 160
Conscience, 55, 135
Consciousness, 55, 56, 57, 58, 66, 81, 84-5, 86, 87, 89-94, 100, 135
Copernicus, 237

Darwin, Charles, 11, 12, 124, 130, 237
Death instincts, 25, 30, 32, 35, 70-4, 144
Death wish, 152, 192
Delboeuf, 184
Delgado, Jose, 218
Democritus, 123
Descartes, René, 123, 129
Dewey, John, 122
Diderot, 124, 130
Disequilibrium, 62
Dreams, 26, 27, 28, 41-5, 53, 54, 98, 103-106, 106-10, 115, 116, 117, 185, 194, 199
Dualism, 22, 23, 123, 125, 131, 160, 161, 175, 184
Du Bois-Raymond, Emil, 11
Dynamic Trauma, 15, 16, 18, 19, 23, 24

Ego, 29, 30, 135, 136, 138, 139, 140, 145, 146
Ego and the Id, Freud, 29
Einstein, Albert, 34, 35
Ellis, Havelock, 118, 120, 222
Encyclopedia of Medicine, 16
Engels, Frederick, 124
Epicurus, 123
Erotogenic zones, 72

249

Evolution, 11, 12, 82, 140
Excitation, 63
Exner, Sigmund, 128
Extinction, 65

Fechner, G. T., 118
Ferrier, David, 209
First signalling system, 88, 106-10, 160
Fistula, dream, 42, 45-9
Fistula, salivary, 40, 41, 42, 43-5
Fixation, 74
Fliess, Wilhelm, 20, 188, 189, 190, 194
Foerster, D., 209
Forgetting, 65
Franklin, Benjamin, 124
Frazer, J. G., 115, 120
Free association, 26, 28, 46, 47, 53, 54, 56, 98
Freud, Amalia, 10
Freud, Jacob, 10, 13
Freud, Sigmund, education of, 10-2; as neurologist, 12-6; in search of dynamic trauma, 16-9; *The Project*, 20-2; discovery of psychoanalysis, 22-5; elaboration of psychoanalysis, 25-9; later years, 29-37; confrontation of second half of his life by the first half, 37-8; method of, 40, 42, 45-9; theory of repression, 53-7; conception of psychic energy, 57-9; theory of instincts, 70-4; three systems of mental apparatus, 79-87; hypnosis, 100-03; sleep and dreams, 103-06; theoretical lineage, 113-22; from primitive mind to civilized mind, 134-45; from infant mind to adult mind, 145-58; genesis of psychoanalysis, 180-5; seductive theory of neurosis, 185-9; self-analysis, 189-96; case histories, 196-205
Fritsch, G., 209
Fulton, J. F., 209

Galileo, 175
Gestalt psychology, 161
Goethe, Wolfgang, 11, 32
Gold chloride method, 13
Goltz, F. Vagus, 127, 209
Griesinger, W., 118
Guilt, 32, 33, 138, 152

Hall, G. Stanley, 31
Hartley, David, 125, 126, 127
Hartmann, Edward von, 121
Hegel, G. W. F., 124
Helmholtz, Herman von, 11, 16, 127, 128, 130
Helvetius, 124
Hemianopsia, 15

Herbart, J. F., 118-20
Herring, Ewald, 127, 128
Hiatus in cerebral physiology, 22, 111
Higher nervous activity, 64, 66, 89-94, 95, 96, 97, 98, 107
Hirschfield, Magnus, 118
History, 33, 34
Hitler, 37
Hitzig, E., 209
Hobbes, Thomas, 123, 124
Holbach, 124
Horsley, V., 209
Human Intellect, James Rush, 20
Hume, David, 125
Hypnosis, 23, 46, 98, 101-3, 106-10, 181-2, 210, 213-4
Hypnotic suggestion, 17, 25, 26, 40, 42, 98, 101-3, 106-10, 114
Hysteria, 15, 18, 181, 182, 183, 184

Id, 29, 136, 137, 138, 139, 140, 145, 146
Idealism, 123, 177, 238
Incest, 32, 33, 136, 140, 150-8
Infantile cerebral paralysis, 16
Infantile sexual phases, 73, 118, 146-9, 192, 193-4, 195
Inferiority of women, 35, 36
Inhibition, 64, 106-10
Instincts, 25, 29, 30, 32, 34, 55, 56, 58, 59; Freud's theory of, 70-4; Pavlov's theory of, 74-8, 81-4, 86, 150-7, 159
Institute of Experimental Medicine, 44
Institute for Children's Diseases, 15
International Psychoanalytical Congress, 31
Interpretation of dreams, 26, 27, 28
Interpretation of Dreams, Freud, 27, 103-6, 110
Introspection, 47, 49, 50, 51

Jackson, Hughlings, 209
James, Williams, 71, 121, 178
Janet, Pierre, 182, 184
Jefferson, Thomas, 124
Jones, Ernest, 12
Jung, C. G., 30, 196

Koehler, Wolfgang, 160, 161, 162, 163, 164, 165, 166
Kraeplin, 209
Krafft-Ebing, 118, 120

La Mettrie, 124
Language, 90-4, 160, 167, 171, 172
Le Bon, Gustave, 115, 116, 120
Leibniz, G. W., 129
Leonardo da Vinci, Freud, 31, 36

INDEX

Libido, 58-61, 141-3, 153
Liébault, A. A., 17, 114, 120
Localization, 86
Locke, John, 116, 124
Logic, 137
Löwenfeld, 118
Luciano, L., 209
Lucretius, 123
Ludwig, Carl, 11, 127, 209

Magnus, R., 76
Male superiority, 35, 36
Marx, Karl, 124, 130, 237
Masodrism, 72
Materialism, 11, 122, 123, 161, 168, 175, 184, 237
Max-Mueller, F., 115, 120
Medulla oblongata, 14
Mental apparatus, 48, 58, 79-87, 100
Mental topography, 80
Mesmer, 17
Metaphysics, 81, 176
Metapsychology, 29, 37, 79, 87, 95, 96, 97, 98, 222
Meynert, Theodore, 14, 119
Mill, James, 125
Moebius, 118, 184
Moses and Monotheism, Freud, 31
Müller, Johannes, 125, 127, 209
Mythology, 74, 115, 116, 134, 136-7, 231

Neuroses, 17, 19, 21, 24, 27, 28, 182, 184, 190, 196, 200, 209, 212, 228
New Lectures on the Diseases of the Nervous System, Charcot, 15
Nietzsche, Frederick, 121, 122
Nothnagel, H., 209

Objectivity, 49, 52
Oedipus complex, 32, 33, 141, 149-57, 140 192, 193, 202, 204

Paine, Thomas, 124
Patricide, 32, 33, 139, 152
Pavlov and Freud, 7-9, 40, 53, 66-8, 69-70, 78, 79, 94-9, 100, 110-2, 113, 131, 132-3, 176-8, 179-80, 215-20, 221-37
Pavlov, I. P., 6, 7, 8, 9, 10, 21, 38, 39, 40, 43-5, 51-2, 61-6, 78, 79, 106-10, 122-31, 159-76, 208-15, 216-20
Penis envy, 154-5, 146
Perception, 64, 169-74
Perversion phenomena, 72
Plato, 123
Preconscious, 80, 81, 83-4, 100, 101, 102
Primal scene, 202-3

Putnam, J. J., 31
Physics, 35
Physiological Institute, 12, 13
Primal horde, myth of, 32, 135
Primordial language, 26
Project, The, 20, 21, 23
Prometheus myth, 136-7
Protective inhibition, 213
Psychic energy, 19, 23, 24, 25, 26, 27; concept of, 57-9, 66
Psychoanalysis, 19, 25, 27, 28, 30, 31, 37, 38, 49, 50, 53, 54, 55, 122, 134, 141, 178, 185, 199, 200, 201, 204, 205, 206, 211, 222, 223, 224, 227, 228 self defense
Psychoanalytical technique, 26, 27, 28
Psycho-dynamics, 60
Psychology and the Analysis of the Ego, Freud, 29
Psychopathology of Everyday Life, Freud, 28
Psychophysical parallelism, 128, 129, 131, 184
Pure psychology, 20, 22, 23

Radestock, P., 114, 120
Rational psychotherapy, 228-9
Raymond, Du Bois, 127
Reality principle, 29, 138
Reflex, 61, 62, 66, 74, 77, 125, 172
Regression, 74
Reichert formula, 13
Reinich, S., 115, 120
Religion, 33
Remembering, 65
Repression, 24, 26, 27, 28, 29, 30, 31, 32, 37, 40; theory of, 53-61, 136, 138, 139, 192
Resistance, 26, 27, 28, 29, 46, 192, 207
Rush, Benjamin, 179
Rush, James, 20, 21, 125, 127
Russell, Bertrand, 222

Sadism, 72
Sâlpetriére, 14, 15, 180-4
Schermer, K. A., 114, 120
Schiff, M., 209
Schiller, F. C. S., 122 .
Schizophrenia, 212-4
Schopenhauer, Arthur, 121, 122
Schrenk-Notzing, 118
Schubert, G. H., 114, 120
Sechenov, I. M., 21, 125, 127, 130, 209
Second signalling system, 88, 89-94, 106-10, 160
Seduction, 28
Sensation, 169-71
Sexual instincts, 25, 30, 32, 56, 57, 58, 70-4, 141, 143, 144

Signalling, 62-5
Sleep, 103-10
Smith, Robertson, 134
Society, 32, 33
Somnambolism, 17
Spencer, Herbert, 74, 125, 130
Steckel, Wilhelm, 118
Stricker, Solomon, 13
Strumpel, 184
Studies in Hysteria, Freud and Brener, 19, 20
Subjectivity, 49, 50, 51, 52
Sublimation, 56, 74, 141, 143
Substitute gratifications, 56
Suggestion and Its Application as a Therapy, Bernheim, 17
Super-ego, 25, 29, 135, 136, 138, 139, 140, 145, 146, 226
Symbol translation, 26, 47, 48, 115, 116, 117, 118, 145, 185, 186, 192, 197
Symptomatic actions, 56
Synthesis, 63-4, 172

Temporary reflex, 62, 63
Tetus, Nicholai, 125
Therapy, 19, 25, 27
Thorndike, E. L., 125, 129, 130
Totem and Taboo, Freud, 31
Transference phenomena, 26, 27, 28, 98

Tsyon, I. F., 127

Unconditional reflex, 43, 62, 63, 74-8, 88-9, 159-60
Unconscious, 19, 22, 25, 26, 27, 28, 29, 30, 32, 33, 34, 40, 54, 56, 81-4, 85, 86, 95, 96, 97, 98, 101-6, 113, 114, 117, 118, 119, 120, 134, 135, 140, 141, 144, 146, 177, 178, 185, 186, 191, 199, 205, 207, 226
Urging method, 23, 26

Vaihinger, Hans, 122
Vienna Academy of Science, 12, 13
Vienna Psychoanalytical Society, 30
Vitalism, 11
Vogts, C., 209
Vogts, O., 209
Voluntarism, 121

War, 34, 35
Watson, J. B., 69
Weber, Ernest Heinrich, 127
Whitehead, A. N., 129
Wit and Its Relation to the Unconscious, Freud, 28
Wundt, Wilhelm, 125, 128, 129, 130

Yearbook of Sexual Aberrations, 118
Yerkes, Robert, 160, 161, 162, 163

Parapraxes, 83
Phylogenetic + Ontogenetic adaptation 131, 140, 145-6, 159, 173,
Mind, Chap IX, (n.b. 164-8), 179,
Analyzers, 170